INTERNATIONAL SERIES OF MONOGRAPHS ON

PURE AND APPLIED MATHEMATICS

GENERAL EDITOR: I. N. SNEDDON

VOLUME 6

HOMOLOGY THEORY
ON ALGEBRAIC VARIETIES

HOMOLOGY THEORY
ON ALGEBRAIC VARIETIES

by

ANDREW H. WALLACE

Assistant Professor of Mathematics
University of Toronto

PERGAMON PRESS

NEW YORK · LONDON
PARIS · LOS ANGELES
1958

PERGAMON PRESS INC.
122 East 55th Street, New York 22, N.Y.
10638 South Wilton Place, Los Angeles 47, California

PERGAMON PRESS LTD.
4 and 5 Fitzroy Square, London W.1.

PERGAMON PRESS S.A.R.L.
24 Rue des Écoles, Paris Vᵉ

Library of Congress Card Number 57–14497

Printed in Northern Ireland at The Universities Press, Belfast

CONTENTS

INTRODUCTION

THIS monograph was originally planned as a series of papers, the first of which has already appeared, namely [11]. The nature of the subject, however, along with the length of the treatment, made it seem more advisable to rearrange the work in book form. The material of [11] appears in a modified form in Chapters I–IV of this monograph.

The main theorems whose proofs are given here were first formulated by Lefschetz in [9], and have since turned out to be of fundamental importance in the topological aspects of algebraic geometry. These theorems may be briefly described as follows. Let V be a non-singular r-dimensional algebraic variety in complex projective space, and let V_0 be a non-singular hyperplane section of V. Then Lefschetz's first main theorem states that all cycles of dimension less than r on V are homologous to cycles on V_0. Now V_0 may be taken as a member of a pencil of hyperplane sections of V, a pencil which contains only a finite number of singular sections. Lefschetz's second main theorem, interpreted in terms of relative homology, shows how to obtain a set of generators for $H_r(V, V_0)$, one of which is associated in a certain way with each of these singular sections. The third main result of Lefschetz concerns the Poincaré formula, which describes the variation of cycles of V_0 as this section is made to vary within a pencil of sections.

The proofs of these theorems are fairly elaborate and involve a considerable amount of verification of intricate detail. In view of this, I have set apart some of the more complicated pieces of working in sections or chapters by themselves, introducing the actual details of the proofs by geometrical descriptions, sometimes aided with diagrams. Thus a descriptive outline of the proofs of the main theorems may be obtained by reading Chapter I, §1 of Chapter II, Chapter III, Chapter IV, Chapter VI and the first four sections of Chapter VIII. Throughout the book singular homology theory will be used, and the coefficient group will be the group of integers, except in Chapter VIII.

I conclude this introductory note with some remarks on other work in this field. Zariski in [13] gives a detailed description of the work [9] of Lefschetz, in so far as it concerns surfaces. In [3] Chow, discussing a variety of any dimension, obtains a result for the fundamental group similar to the first main theorem of Lefschetz stated above. A different formulation of the theory, in terms of cohomology and making use of the technique of spectral sequences, is given by Fary in [5]. The theorems as stated in the present monograph are treated essentially from a geometrical point of view, but it will be realised that there is a close link with the transcendental theory of algebraic varieties. For a discussion of the relationship between the two approaches, see Hodge [7].

CHAPTER I

LINEAR SECTIONS OF AN ALGEBRAIC VARIETY

1. Hyperplane sections of a non-singular variety

The main tool in this work is the fibring of a variety by linear sections. As a preparation for this, some results will be worked out concerning the linear, and, in particular, the hyperplane sections of a non-singular variety W defined over an arbitrary field k of characteristic zero and contained in projective n-space. It will be assumed that W is of dimension r and is absolutely irreducible.

Let L^n be the projective space containing W and let L'^n be the dual projective space, that is to say the space whose points represent the hyperplanes of L^n, the hyperplane with equation $\sum_{i=1}^{n+1} v_i X_i = 0$ being represented by the point $(v) = (v_1, v_2, \ldots, v_{n+1})$. For convenience the hyperplane represented by the point (v) of L'^n will be called the hyperplane (v).

The hyperplane (v) will be called a tangent hyperplane to W at the point $(x) = (x_1, x_2, \ldots, x_{n+1})$ if and only if it contains the tangent linear variety $T(x)$ to W at (x); since W is non-singular, $T(x)$ exists for all (x) on W. Note that this concept of tangent hyperplane reduces to the usual one when W is a hypersurface of L^n.

If (x) is a generic point of W and (v) is a generic tangent hyperplane to W at (x) (that is to say a generic hyperplane passing through $T(x)$), then (v) has a locus W' in L'^n. W' is an absolutely irreducible variety of dimension not greater than $n - 1$ (in other words it cannot fill the whole space L'^n). Also it is not hard to see that every hyperplane (v') which is a tangent hyperplane to W at some point is a specialization of (v) over k. W' is called the dual of W.

Since W is non-singular, it follows easily by taking a

1

suitable affine model and using the Jacobian criterion for a singularity, that (v) is a tangent hyperplane to W at a point (x) if and only if (x) is a singularity of the intersection $(v) \cap W$. Thus W' represents the set of hyperplanes whose sections with W have at least one singular point. The fact that the dimension of W' is not greater than $n - 1$ can therefore be stated as follows:

LEMMA a. *A generic hyperplane of L^n cuts W in a non-singular variety.*

Combining this with the fact that a generic hyperplane section of an absolutely irreducible variety is absolutely irreducible, it follows at once by induction that:

LEMMA b. *The intersection of W with a generic linear variety of any dimension is non-singular.*

Consider now a generic pencil Π of hyperplanes in L^n; that is to say, the set of hyperplanes corresponding by duality to the points of a generic line l in L'^n. If the dimension of W' is less than $n - 1$, l will not meet W', and it will follow that all the members of Π will cut non-singular sections on W. If, on the other hand, W' is of dimension $n - 1$, l will meet W' in a finite number of points all simple on W'. Now a classical argument shows that, if (v) is a simple point of W' (assumed of dimension $n - 1$) then the tangent hyperplane to W' at (v) corresponds by duality to the point (which is consequently unique) at which (v) is a tangent hyperplane for W. In other words if (v) is a simple point of W', the intersection $(v) \cap W$ has exactly one singular point. This argument applies to each intersection of l and W'. And so, summing up:

LEMMA c. *A generic hyperplane pencil Π in L^n either cuts all non-singular sections on W or cuts at most a finite number of singular sections each of which has exactly one singular point.*

2. A family of linear sections of W

It will turn out later in this work that the cases in which the dimension of W' is less than or is equal to $n - 1$ usually require separate attention. Until further notice, then, it will be assumed that the dimension of W' is exactly $n - 1$.

Let L be an $(s-1)$-dimensional linear subspace of L^n, and let Λ denote the family of all s-dimensional linear spaces through L. The members of Λ can be set in one-one correspondence with the points of an $(n-s)$-dimensional projective space L_0. In fact, for the sake of definiteness it will be assumed that L_0 is a subspace of L^n not meeting L and each member of Λ corresponds to the point in which it meets L_0.

If, now, L is a generic $(s-1)$-space it is clear that a generic member of Λ is actually a generic s-space in L^n, and consequently cuts a non-singular section on W. Also the conditions for a linear variety to cut W in a singular section are expressible (using the Jacobian condition) by polynomial equations in the coefficients of the equations of the linear variety. It follows at once that L can be chosen with equations having coefficients in k in such a way that the generic member of Λ cuts a non-singular section on W. And in addition, the members of Λ cutting singular sections on W will correspond, in the manner just described, to the points of a bunch of varieties Γ in L_0.

It will now be shown that the bunch Γ consists of exactly one absolutely irreducible variety, if L is suitably chosen (always under the assumption that W' is of dimension $n-1$). Let L' be the linear $(n-s)$-dimensional variety in L'^n which corresponds by duality to L. It will be assumed that s satisfies the inequality $n-r < s < n-1$. This condition excludes the case in which Λ is a hyperplane pencil, when Γ reduces to a finite set of points, and also ensures that the sections of W by members of Λ will be varieties of positive dimension, and not simply finite sets of points. If L, and so L', is generic, the intersection $W' \cap L'$ will be an absolutely irreducible variety not lying entirely in the singular variety of W', and the condition for this not to happen is a set of polynomial equations in the coefficients of the equations of L. It may therefore be assumed that L is chosen with equations over k in such a way that, in addition to satisfying the conditions already laid on it earlier in this section, the intersection $L' \cap W'$ is absolutely irreducible and has a generic point which is simple on W'.

Let (v) be a generic point of $L' \cap W'$ over k. Since (v) is simple on W', the tangent hyperplane to W' at (v) is defined, and, as pointed out in §1, corresponds by duality to the singular point of the intersection of W and the hyperplane (v). Let this singular point be (x); then clearly the ratios of the homogeneous coordinates $x_1, x_2, \ldots, x_{n+1}$ are in $k(v)$, the field generated over k by the ratios of the v. Let (y) be the intersection with L_0 of the linear s-space $L(x)$ joining L and the point (x). $L(x)$ is a member of Λ. Also, since (v) is a point of L', the hyperplane (v) contains L, and (x) too, by the definition of (x), and hence $L(x)$. But (x) is singular on $(v) \cap W$; and so $L(x)$ cuts W in a variety having (x) as a singular point. From this it follows that (y) is a point of Γ. On the other hand it has been mentioned that $k(x) \subset k(v)$; and since (y) is the intersection of $L(x)$ and L (which can be assumed to be defined over k), $k(y) \subset k(x)$. Hence the ratios of the coordinates of (y) are in $k(v)$, which is a regular extension of k (since $W' \cap L'$ is absolutely irreducible) and from this it follows that $k(y)$ is a regular extension of k. Thus (y) is the generic point of an absolutely irreducible variety Γ_0, and from what has been said it follows that $\Gamma_0 \subset \Gamma$.

It will now be shown that $\Gamma_0 = \Gamma$. Let (y') be any point of Γ; it is required to prove that (y') is in Γ_0, that is to say, that (y') is a specialization of (y) over k. (The term specialization here means the specialization of the ratios of the coordinates rather than of the coordinates themselves.)

The definition of Γ implies that, since $(y') \in \Gamma$, the linear s-space $L(y')$ joining L and (y') cuts a singular section on W. Let (x') be a singular point of the intersection $L(y') \cap W$. Consideration of the Jacobian condition for a singularity shows at once that there is at least one hyperplane (v') containing $L(x')$ and cutting on W a singular section having a singularity at (x'). In other words, (v') is a tangent hyperplane to W at (x'). It is not hard to see from this that (v', x') is a specialization of (v, x) over k; and so (x') is a specialization of (x). On the other hand, (y) is the intersection of L_0 and the join of L to (x) while (y') is the intersection of L_0 and the join of L to (x'), from which it follows at once that (x', y') is a specialization of (x, y) over k. In particular, (y') is a specialization of (y). (y') is any point of Γ, and so it has been shown that $\Gamma \subset \Gamma_0$. It is already known that $\Gamma_0 \subset \Gamma$ and so $\Gamma_0 = \Gamma$, as was to be shown.

Γ has thus been shown to be an absolutely irreducible variety in L_0, (y) being a generic point. It will now be checked that, if L is chosen suitably, the linear s-space joining L and (y) cuts on W a section having exactly one singular point. This will be proved with the aid of the following lemma:

LEMMA d. *If W is a variety of projective n-space L^n with a dual W' of dimension $n - 1$, and if H is a generic hyperplane of L^n, represented dually in L'^n by the point H', then the dual of $W \cap H$ is the cone of tangent lines from H' to W'.*

PROOF. Let (x) be a generic point of $W \cap H$; (x) is of course, at the same time, a generic point of W. Let $T_0(x) = T(x) \cap H$; here $T(x)$ is the tangent linear variety to W at (x) and it is easy to see that $T_0(x)$ is the tangent linear variety to $W \cap H$ at this point. Let (v_0) be a generic tangent hyperplane to $W \cap H$ at (x). This means that (v_0) contains $T_0(x)$. It is then clear that every hyperplane of the pencil determined by H and (v_0) contains $T_0(x)$, and is therefore a tangent hyperplane to $W \cap H$ at (x). In other words, the line in L'^n joining H' to the point (v_0) lies in the dual of $W \cap H$. The latter variety is therefore a cone of vertex H'.

On the other hand, the pencil determined by H and the hyperplane (v_0) contains exactly one hyperplane (v) which contains $T(x)$; namely the hyperplane determined by the intersection $H \cap (v_0)$ and a point of $T(x)$ not on that intersection. (v) is then a point of W'. If it is a simple point then, as has already been remarked, the tangent hyperplane to W' (supposed to be of dimension $n - 1$) at (v) corresponds by duality to (x). But, since (x) is in the hyperplane H, it follows that the tangent hyperplane to W' at (v) passes through H'. That is to say, the join of H' and (v), or H' and (v_0), is a tangent line to W', provided that (v) is simple on W'. It has thus been shown that the generic generator of the cone dual to $W \cap H$ is either a tangent line to W' or the join of H' to a singular point of W'.

The proof will be completed by showing that any tangent line to W' from H' lies in the dual of $W \cap H$. To do this, let (v) be the point of contact of some tangent line to W' from H', (v) being, of course, simple on W'. Then the hyperplane (v) cuts on W a section with just one singularity (x), namely the point corresponding by duality to the tangent hyperplane to W' at (v). Then the hyperplane (v) contains $T(x)$, and so, if (w) is any point on the join of H' and the point (v), the hyperplane (w) will contain the intersection of H and the hyperplane (v), and so will contain $H \cap T(x) = T_0(x)$. Thus the tangent line from H' touching W' at (v) is contained in the dual of $H \cap W$. This completes the proof of the lemma.

The consequence of this lemma which is wanted for the present purpose is that the assumption that W' is of dimension $n - 1$ implies that the dual of $H \cap W$ is also of dimension $n - 1$. Also it is clear that the lemma, and so this corollary of it, will hold for a non-generic H, just so long as the intersection $H \cap W$ is absolutely irreducible, and this is true provided that the coefficients of the equation of H do not satisfy certain polynomial equations.

Repeated application of the result just proved yields the following:

LEMMA e. *If W' is of dimension $n - 1$ and L_1 is a linear space whose intersection with W is absolutely irreducible, then the dual of $W \cap L_1$ is of dimension $n - 1$.*

Return now to the family Λ of s-spaces through L in L^n, and in particular to those members of Λ corresponding to the points of the variety Γ. It is easy to see that L can be chosen so that, in addition to satisfying the conditions which have already been required of it, a generic linear $(s + 1)$-space L_1 through L cuts W in an absolutely irreducible non-singular variety. Lemma e then applies to $W \cap L_1$, which has thus an $(n - 1)$-dimensional dual. By Lemma c, a suitably chosen hyperplane pencil cuts $W \cap L_1$ in at most a finite number of singular sections, each with exactly one singular point. Moreover it is not hard to see that a pencil whose axis contains L will do, provided that the equations of L do not satisfy certain polynomial equations, and it will now be assumed that they do not. Finally it is clear that the members of this pencil cut L_1 in members of Λ corresponding to a generic line in L_0. Such a line therefore cuts Γ in a finite number of points, each corresponding to a member of Λ cutting W in a section with just one singularity. Each of these points on Γ is generic on Γ, and it has, incidentally, been shown that Γ is of dimension $n - s - 1$. Summing up now all that has been proved:

THEOREM 1. *If the linear $(s - 1)$-space L is suitably chosen, if $n - r < s < n - 1$, and if W' is of dimension $n - 1$, then Γ, whose points correspond to members of Λ cutting singular sections on W, is an absolutely irreducible variety of dimension $n - s - 1$ (i.e. a hypersurface of the space L_0), and a generic point of Γ corresponds to a member of Λ cutting on W a section with just one singularity.*

3. The fibring of a variety defined over the complex numbers

The notations of §2 will still be used, with the exception that W will now be replaced by an irreducible non-singular variety V defined over the complex numbers. Let V be of dimension r, and for the moment assume that the dual of V is of dimension $n - 1$. Let L be a linear $(s - 1)$-dimensional space, whose equations have complex coefficients, chosen in one of the following ways. Either $s = n - 1$, and L is the axis of a pencil Π of hyperplanes satisfying Lemma c in relation to V. Or $n - r < s < n - 1$, and the family of s-spaces through L satisfies Theorem 1 in relation to V. Note that in the first alternative L_0 becomes a linear 1-space, that is, topologically speaking, a sphere, and Γ becomes a finite set of points.

Some terminology and notation will now be introduced. The points of L_0 not on Γ will be called ordinary points, while those of Γ will be called special (these terms being used in both cases, $s = n - 1$ and $s < n - 1$). If p is any point of L_0, ordinary or special, $V(p)$ will denote the section cut on V by the member of Λ corresponding to p. Also if A is any set of points on L_0, $V(A)$ will denote the union of all the $V(p)$ for $p \in A$. P will denote the intersection $L \cap V$. L can be chosen, simply by ensuring that the coefficients of its equations do not satisfy certain polynomial equations, so that P is non-singular. It will be assumed that this choice has been made. Note that this implies that any singularities of any of the $V(p)$, $p \in \Gamma$, will certainly not lie on P.

The object of the present section is to examine $V(K)$, where K is a subset of L_0 consisting entirely of ordinary points. The main result is that $V(K)$ bears a close relation to a certain fibre bundle, the sections $V(p)$ for $p \in K$ corresponding to the fibres.

It will be convenient for this purpose to introduce a special coordinate system in L^n. Complex homogeneous coordinates $(z_1, z_2, \ldots, z_{n+1})$ will be chosen in L^n in such a way that the equations of L are $z_1 = z_2 = \ldots = z_{n-s} = z_{n+1} = 0$. The members of Λ not lying in the hyperplane $z_{n+1} = 0$ will then have equations of the form $z_i = \zeta_i z_{n+1}$, $i = 1, 2, \ldots, n - s$. Moreover, in discussing any particular member of Λ, corresponding say to $p \in L_0$, it can be assumed that the coordinates are chosen in such a way that no member of Λ corresponding to a point near p lies in $z_{n+1} = 0$. For discussing such s-spaces through L, it can therefore be assumed that the homogeneous coordinates are normalized with $z_{n+1} = 1$. The members of Λ will then have equations $z_i = \zeta_i$, $i = 1, 2, \ldots, n - s$.

With the arrangement of coordinates just made, z_1, $z_2, \ldots, z_{n-s}$ can be taken as affine coordinates on L_0. And so the section of V by the s-space $z_i = \zeta_i$, $i = 1, 2, \ldots, n - s$, can be written as $V(\zeta_1, \zeta_2, \ldots, \zeta_{n-s})$ or more briefly as $V(\zeta)$; this is simply a modification of the notation already introduced for such sections.

Now V, being a non-singular algebraic variety in complex projective space, is a compact complex analytic manifold, and so also a real analytic manifold. And since an analytic

Riemann metric can be constructed on a complex projective space it follows that the same is true of V. Assume then that V is given a Riemann metric whose coefficients in terms of any local coordinate system are real analytic functions of these coordinates. Using this metric, geodesics can be constructed on V.

The section $V(\zeta)$, for an ordinary point (ζ) of L_0, is a compact submanifold of V of dimension $2(r - n + s)$, and so a sufficiently small neighbourhood B of $V(\zeta)$ may be entirely filled by geodesic arcs orthogonal to $V(\zeta)$, in such a way that the union of points of all the arcs through any point of $V(\zeta)$ is an open $(2n - 2s)$-cell, and through each point of $B - V(\zeta)$ passes exactly one such arc. Modifying B if necessary it can be arranged that all the geodesic arcs in question are of length δ say. B thus has the structure of a fibre bundle of base $V(\zeta)$ and fibre a $(2n - 2s)$-cell; the fibres in B are the $(2n - 2s)$-dimensional surface elements formed by geodesics normal to $V(\zeta)$ at points of $V(\zeta)$. If attention is to be drawn to the base of B and the radius of its fibres, it will be denoted by $B(\zeta, \delta)$, and will be called the normal bundle to $V(\zeta)$ of radius δ. (For further details concerning the normal bundle of a submanifold in a given manifold see Cairns [2].)

Associated with the idea of the normal bundle to $V(\zeta)$ is the idea of a normal neighbourhood of a point p on $V(\zeta)$. Here $V(\zeta)$ may be a singular section of V, with $(\zeta) \in \Gamma$, but p must be a non-singular point on it. Let U be any neighbourhood of p on $V(\zeta)$ such that all points of U are non-singular on $V(\zeta)$. Then a normal neighbourhood of p in V is the point-set union of all the geodesic arcs of some fixed length δ normal to $V(\zeta)$ at points of U. δ is called the radius of the normal neighbourhood. If W is a normal neighbourhood of p on $V(\zeta)$ constructed over the neighbourhood U in $V(\zeta)$, then W is the topological product of U and an open $(2n - 2s)$-cell. In fact, if (ξ) denotes an admissible coordinate system around p on $V(\zeta)$, then there is a set of admissible coordinates in W of the form (ξ, u), where $(u) = (u_1, u_2, \ldots, u_{2n-2s})$ specify the displacement from $V(\zeta)$.

K being a set of ordinary points on L_0, the next step is to construct a bundle $B(\zeta, \delta(\zeta))$ for each $(\zeta) \in K$. It will be shown that, for (z) sufficiently near (ζ) on L_0, $V(z)$ is an analytic cross section of $B(\zeta, \delta(\zeta))$. This is to be done for each (ζ) in K. K will thus have a covering $\{N_\zeta\}$ such that, for $(z) \in N_\zeta$, $V(z)$ is an analytic cross-section of $B(\zeta, \delta(\zeta))$. The idea is then to regard $V(N_\zeta)$ as obtained from $V(\zeta) \times N_\zeta$ by compressing the subset $P \times N_\zeta$ into P. That is to say, for each (ζ) a mapping will be constructed of $V(\zeta) \times N_\zeta$ onto $V(N_\zeta)$, and finally the sets $V(\zeta) \times N_\zeta$ will be put together to form a fibre bundle $X(K)$ over K as base in such a way that the mappings just mentioned fit together to form a continuous mapping $\psi : X(K) \to V(K)$. The essential property of ψ will be that it is a homeomorphism if P is removed from $V(K)$ and from each fibre of $X(K)$. The details of the operation just described will now be carried out in the following sequence of lemmas and theorems.

LEMMA a. (1) *Let p be a non-singular point of $V(\zeta)$ ((ζ) not necessarily an ordinary point) not on P and not on $z_{n+1} = 0$, the equations of the members of Λ being $z_i = \zeta_i z_{n+1}$, $i = 1$, $2, \ldots, n - s$. Then complex local coordinates on V, regarded as a complex analytic manifold, can be chosen around p to include $z_1, z_2, \ldots, z_{n-s}$; here z_{n+1} is normalized to equal 1.*

(2) *Let $p \in P$. Then complex local coordinates on V around p can be taken to include $z_1, z_2, \ldots, z_{n-s}, z_{n+1}$, some coordinate other than these being set equal to 1.*

(3) *In terms of the local coordinates of part (1) of this lemma, $V(\zeta)$ has, locally around p, the equations $z_i = \zeta_i$; in terms of the local coordinates of part (2) the corresponding local equations are $z_i = \zeta_i z_{n+1}$, i running from 1 to $n - s$ in each case.*

PROOF. This is an immediate consequence of the condition for a point to be simple on a variety along with the implicit function theorem.

If p is a point not on P and if p is a simple point on $V(\zeta)$, where (ζ) is any point of L_0, then, in the first place, the above lemma implies that there is a system of real local coordinates around p of the form $(x, y) = (x_1, x_2, \ldots, x_{2n-2s}, y_1, y_2, \ldots,$

$y_{2r-2n+2s})$ where $z_j = x_{2j-1} + ix_{2j}, j = 1, 2, \ldots, n - s$. In the second place, it has already been seen that, in a normal neighbourhood of p, there are local coordinates of the form $(\xi, u) = (\xi, u_1, u_2, \ldots, u_{2n-2s})$. Then:

LEMMA b. *If $p \in V(\zeta)$, $p \notin P$, and (x, y), (ξ, u) are the coordinate systems just mentioned, then (ξ, x) is also an admissible coordinate system around p.*

PROOF. The values of (ξ, x) for a point q near p are understood to be calculated by noting on which section $V(z)$ q lies, this giving the values of the x_i, and then taking as values of (ξ) the coordinates of the foot (on $V(\zeta)$) of the geodesic arc through q normal to $V(\zeta)$. The proof may be carried out by writing down the differential equations of the geodesics in terms of the local coordinates (x, y) and considering as initial conditions orthogonality to $V(\zeta)$ at points near p on $V(\zeta)$. If s denotes geodesic arc-length, these conditions allow the dx_i/ds to be given arbitrary values $\alpha_1, \alpha_2, \ldots, \alpha_{2n-2s}$ for $s = 0$. As usual in the construction of normal coordinates, the $\alpha_i s$ ($i = 1, 2, \ldots, 2n - 2s$) are the coordinates u_i and the equations of the geodesics may be written down as power series in the u_i with coefficients depending on the initial point on $V(\zeta)$. If this process is carried out explicitly, it turns out that the condition of orthogonality to $V(\zeta)$ implies the non-vanishing at p of the Jacobian of the coordinates (ξ, x) with respect to (ξ, u), and this gives the required result.

LEMMA c. *Let $p \in P$ and let (ξ, u) be a normal coordinate system in a normal neighbourhood of p over some neighbourhood on $V(\zeta)$, (ζ) being any point of L_0. Then the linear section $V(z)$ has locally the equations*

$$u_i = f_i(\xi, x), \qquad i = 1, 2, \ldots, 2n - 2s,$$

where the f_i are real analytic functions of their arguments when (ξ) is sufficiently near to p on $V(\zeta)$ and (z) is sufficiently near to (ζ) on L_0, the x_i being defined by $z_j = x_{2j-1} + ix_{2j}$, $j = 1, 2, \ldots, n - s$.

PROOF. Let complex local coordinates be taken around p on V as in part (2) of Lemma a (noting that the z_i appearing there are not the same as those in the statement of this lemma) and let $y_1, y_2, \ldots, y_{2n-2s+2}$ be the real and imaginary parts of the z_i named there. Then the y_i belong to a system of real analytic coordinates around p. Part (3) of Lemma a implies that, in terms of these local coordinates, the equations of $V(z)$ are:

$$y_{2i-1} = x_{2i-1}y_{2n-2s+1} - x_{2i}y_{2n-2s+2}$$

$$y_{2i} = x_{2i-1}y_{2n-2s+2} + x_{2i}y_{2n-2s+1}$$

where $i = 1, 2, \ldots, n - s$. Substitute for the y_i in terms of the coordinates (ξ, u); this is done by writing down the analytical expressions for the geodesics normal to $V(\zeta)$, parametrized by arc-length s, and introducing the u_i as $\alpha_i s$ in the manner indicated in the proof of Lemma b. If the equations for $V(z)$ obtained from this substitution are $\phi_i(\xi, u) = 0$, $i = 1, 2, \ldots, 2n - 2s$, then the condition of orthogonality of the geodesics to $V(\zeta)$ implies that, for (z) sufficiently near to (ζ) in L_0, the Jacobian $\left|\dfrac{\partial \phi_i}{\partial u_j}\right|$ is not zero at p. The equations $\phi_i = 0$ can therefore be solved for the u_j to give the required result.

LEMMA d. *If (z) is sufficiently near (ζ) on L_0, $V(z)$ lies entirely inside the normal bundle $B(\zeta, \delta)$ for preassigned $\delta > 0$, (ζ) being an ordinary point of L_0.*

PROOF. If the theorem were false there would be a sequence $(z^{(1)}), (z^{(2)}), \ldots$ of points on L_0 tending to (ζ) such that each $V(z^{(i)})$ contains a point p_i outside $B(\zeta, \delta)$. The p_i will have a limit point p, necessarily outside $B(\zeta, \delta)$, and it may as well be assumed that a subsequence has already been picked out so that p_i tends to p as a limit. Take complex coordinates around p including $z_1, z_2, \ldots, z_{n-s}$ (cf. Lemma a, (1)); this can be done since $p \notin B(\zeta, \delta)$ and so $p \notin P$. Then for sufficiently large i, the $z_1, z_2, \ldots, z_{n-s}$ coordinates of p_i, namely $z_1^{(i)}, z_2^{(i)}, \ldots, z_{n-s}^{(i)}$ will tend to the corresponding coordinates of p, namely $\zeta_1, \zeta_2, \ldots, \zeta_{n-s}$, as limits. This would imply $p \in V(\zeta)$, which is a contradiction.

THEOREM 2. *If* (z) *is sufficiently near the ordinary point* (ζ) *of* L_0, $V(z)$ *is an analytic cross-section of* $B(\zeta, \delta)$.

PROOF. To each $p \in V(\zeta)$ assign a neighbourhood U_p, in V, as follows:

If $p \in P$, U_p is a normal neighbourhood of radius δ, in which $V(z)$ has, locally, the equations $u_i = f_i^{(p)}(\xi, x)$, $i = 1, 2, \ldots$ ' $2n - 2s$, the $f_i^{(p)}$ being analytic in their arguments and the point $(\xi, f_1^{(p)}, f_2^{(p)}, \ldots, f_{2n-2s}^{(p)})$ lying in U_p for $(\xi) \in U_p \cap V(\xi)$ and the distance of (z) from (ζ) less than k_p, say. (cf. Lemma c above.)

If $p \notin P$, let U_p be a coordinate neighbourhood for local coordinates (ξ, x) around p (cf. Lemma b above), defined by making (ξ) lie in a neighbourhood of p on $V(\zeta)$, and making the distance of (z) from (ζ) on L_0 less than k_p.

By the compactness of $V(\zeta)$, the covering $\{U_p \cap V(\zeta)\}$ may be assumed to be reduced to a finite covering. Let k be less than all the k_p, now finite in number, and also so small that $V(z) \subset B(\zeta, \delta)$ whenever the distance of (z) from (ζ) is less than k (Lemma d).

Now for (z) at distance less than k from (ζ), define the mapping $f_{z\zeta} : V(\zeta) \to V(z)$ by making $f_{z\zeta}(p)$ the point of intersection of $V(z)$ and the fibre of $B(\zeta, \delta)$ through p. The fact that $f_{z\zeta}(p)$ is uniquely defined in this way (and this is the main point of the theorem) can be seen at once by inspecting a neighbourhood U_q in which p lies, where U_q is one of the above constructed neighbourhoods. The analytic property of $f_{z\zeta}$ follows easily from local considerations in one of the U_q.

COROLLARY 1. *It follows at once from the above proof that, for* (z) *sufficiently near* (ζ), $f_{z\zeta}$ *depends analytically on* x_1, $x_2, \ldots, x_{2n-2s}$, *the real and imaginary parts of the coordinates of* (z) *on* L_0.

COROLLARY 2. *If* (ζ) *and* (ζ') *are ordinary points of* L_0, $V(\zeta)$ *and* $V(\zeta')$ *are analytically homeomorphic.*

For (ζ) and (ζ') can be joined by a finite chain of neighbourhoods in each of which Theorem 2 can be applied.

Let V_0 be a fixed non-singular section of V by a member of Λ. By Corollary 2 of Theorem 2 there is an analytic homeomorphism $\phi_\zeta : V(\zeta) \to V_0$, where (ζ) is any ordinary point of L_0. Let $\pi_\zeta : B(\zeta, \delta) \to V(\zeta)$ be the projection mapping in the bundle $B(\zeta, \delta)$. By Theorem 2, there is a neighbourhood N_ζ of (ζ) on L_0 such that $f_{z\zeta}$ is defined and analytic for $(z) \in N_\zeta$. If (ζ') is a second ordinary point on L_0 define $N_{\zeta'}$ similarly and suppose that $N_\zeta \cap N_{\zeta'} \neq \emptyset$. Take $(z) \in N_\zeta \cap N_{\zeta'}$ and define $\phi_{\zeta\zeta}(z) = \phi_\zeta \pi_\zeta f_{z\zeta'} \overset{-1}{\phi_{\zeta'}}$.

THEOREM 3. $\phi_{\zeta\zeta'}(z)$ is an analytic homeomorphism of V_0 onto itself leaving P invariant, and $\phi_{\zeta\zeta'}(z, p)$, for $p \in V_0$, depends analytically on the real and imaginary parts of the coordinates $(z_1, z_2, \ldots, z_{n-s})$ of (z) in L_0.

PROOF. This result follows at once from the analyticity of ϕ_ζ, $\overset{-1}{\phi_{\zeta'}}$, π_ζ and from Theorem 2 and its first corollary.

Let G be the group of all analytic homeomorphisms of V_0 onto itself leaving P invariant. G can be made in a natural manner into a topological group acting continuously on V. Theorem 3 moreover implies that $\phi_{\zeta\zeta'}$ is a continuous mapping of $N_\zeta \cap N_{\zeta'}$ into G. The functions $\phi_{\zeta\zeta'}$ for varying (ζ) and (ζ') are now to be used as transition functions of a fibre bundle with fibre V_0 and group G.

Let K be a subset of L_0 consisting entirely of ordinary points, and let K be contained in the union of a collection of neighbourhoods of the type N_ζ, that is to say, such that $f_{z\zeta}$ is defined as in Theorem 2 for $(z) \in N_\zeta$. For each pair (ζ), (ζ') such that $N_\zeta \cap N_{\zeta'} \cap K \neq \emptyset$, $\phi_{\zeta\zeta'}$ is a continuous mapping of $N_\zeta \cap N_{\zeta'} \cap K$ into G, and it is easy to see that the transitivity condition required of transition functions is satisfied by the $\phi_{\zeta\zeta'}$. Hence there is a fibre bundle $X(K)$ with base K, fibre V_0, group G, defined by the covering $\{N_\zeta \cap K\}$ of K and the transition functions $\phi_{\zeta\zeta'}$ (cf. Steenrod [10]).

In addition, since G acts as identity on P it follows that each fibre of $X(K)$ contains a subspace homeomorphic to P and that the union of these subspaces is homeomorphic to $K \times P$. This subspace $K \times P$ of $X(K)$ will be denoted by $X'(K)$. The main result already promised can now be proved:

THEOREM 4. *There is a continuous mapping* $\psi : X(K) \to V(K)$

which acts as a homeomorphism on $X(K) - X'(K)$, mapping this set onto $V(K) - P$.

PROOF. Take $p \in X(K)$ and let $V_0 \times (N_\zeta \cap K)$ be a local product representation of $X(K)$, such that the projection (z) of p is in $N_\zeta \cap K$. Then, using the maps $f_{z\zeta}$ and ϕ_ζ introduced above let $p = (p_0, z) \in V_0 \times (N_\zeta \cap K)$ and define $\psi(p) = f_{z\zeta}\overset{-1}{\phi_\zeta}(p_0)$. It is not hard to see that ψ is continuous and is independent of the particular choice of local representation of $X(K)$, on account of the special choice of transition functions in $X(K)$.

Now restrict ψ to $X(K) - X'(K)$. $\overset{-1}{\phi_\zeta}$ and $f_{z\zeta}$, for fixed (z), are both homeomorphisms and so if $p \notin X'(K)$, $\psi(p) \notin P$. Define $\overset{-1}{\psi}$ as the mapping $q \to (\phi_\zeta \pi_\zeta q, z)$ where $q \in V(z) \subset B(\zeta, \delta)$.

It can again be checked that this definition of $\overset{-1}{\psi}$ in terms of a local product representation of $X(K)$ is actually a well defined mapping of $V(K) - P \to X(K) - X'(K)$, is continuous, and is the inverse of ψ.

COROLLARY. *Since the restrictions of $\overset{-1}{\phi_\zeta}$ and $f_{z\zeta}$ to P are both the identity it follows from the above proof that the restriction of ψ to $X'(K) = K \times P$ is the natural projection on P.*

Theorem 4 implies that a covering homotopy theorem holds in $V(K)$. The actual form in which this is to be used is the following:

THEOREM 5. *Let K and K' be subsets of L_0 consisting entirely of ordinary points. Let f_0 and f_1 be homotopic mappings of K into K', and let $F_0 : V(K) \to V(K')$ be a mapping which acts as the identity on P, and is such that, for $(z) \in K$, $p \in V(z)$, then $F_0(p) \in V(f_0(z))$. Then there exists a mapping $F_1 : V(K) \to V(K')$, homotopic to F_0, and such that:*

(1) If $f' : K \times I \to K'$ and $F' : V(K) \times I \to V(K')$ define the homotopies of f_0 and F_0 to f_1 and F_1 respectively, then, for $(z) \in K$, the image under F' of $V(z) \times \{t\}$ is the section $V(f'(z, t))$ for all $t \in I$.

(2) F' being as in (1), $F'(q, t) = q$ for all $q \in P$ and all $t \in I$.

PROOF. The proof is a modification of the usual proof of the covering homotopy theorem for fibre bundles. As in the proof for bundles (cf. Steenrod [10]) the idea is to construct the homotopy F' in stages over a sequence of subintervals of I, each stage being broken down into the construction over a sequence of neighbourhoods covering K. The object is, of course, to break the theorem down to a sequence of operations over coordinate neighbourhoods, that is to say neighbourhoods on the base space over which the bundle is locally a product. Here the N_ζ correspond to the coordinate neighbourhoods. It is clear that each of the stages in the construction of F' can be carried out if the following lemma is true.

LEMMA. *Let N_ζ and $N_{\zeta'}$ be two neighbourhoods on L_0 as described before Theorem 3. Let A, B, B' be subsets of N_ζ such that B is a relatively closed set of A and B' is a relatively open set of A containing B and let F be a given mapping of $A \times I$ into $N_{\zeta'}$. Also let F_0' be a mapping of $(V(B') \times I) \cup (V(A) \times \{0\})$ $\to V(N_{\zeta'})$ with the property that $F_0'(V(z) \times \{t\})$, when defined, is the section $V(F(z, t))$. Then F_0' can be extended to a mapping $F' : V(A) \times I \to V(N_{\zeta'})$ with the same covering property and with the property that F' agrees with F_0' on $V(B) \times I$. In addition, given that $F_0'(p, t) = p$ for all p in P and all t in I, F' has the same property.*

The connection of this with the main theorem is that N_ζ is supposed to be one of a collection of such neighbourhoods covering K, $N_{\zeta'}$ being one of a covering of K', $A = K \cap N_\zeta$ and B' is the intersection of K with members of the covering over which the covering homotopy has already been defined. Also it is assumed that there is a second covering $\{U_\zeta\}$ of K with the property that $\bar{U}_\zeta \subset N_\zeta$. B is to be the intersection of K with the closures of those sets of this second covering over which the covering homotopy has already been defined.

PROOF OF LEMMA. Urysohn's Lemma implies the existence of a continuous real valued function ϕ on A taking values between 0 and 1 and equal to 1 on B and to 0 on $A - B'$. Now to define $F'(p, t)$ for a point (p, t) of $V(A) \times I$, suppose first that $p \notin P$. Let $p \in V(z)$, and let $F(z, t) = (z')$. Then set $F'(p, t) = f_{z't'}\pi_{t'}F_0'(p, \phi(z)t)$; $\phi(z)$ is defined here since $p \in V(A)$, and so $(z) \in A$. The definition of F' is completed by setting $F'(p, t) = p$ if $p \in P$. The various requirements on F' stated in the lemma are trivially satisfied, except for the continuity at points (p, t) where $p \in P$. The continuity at such a point follows easily, however, from the fact that the continuity of F_0' at a point (p, t) with $p \in P$ implies the existence, corresponding to a preassigned neighbourhood U of p, of a neighbourhood U_0 of p such that $F'(p', t') \in U$ for all $p' \in U_0$ and all $t' \in I$. This completes the proof of the lemma, and so the sketch of the proof of Theorem 5.

4. Homology groups related to $V(K)$

The object of the present section is to compare certain homology groups related to $V(K)$, K consisting entirely of ordinary points, with the corresponding groups related to the bundle $X(K)$. The following topological lemma will be useful for this purpose, and also in later sections.

SHRINKING LEMMA. *Let A be space and B a subspace, and suppose that there is a family F of curves in A satisfying the following conditions:*

(1) *There is exactly one member of F through each point of $A - B$.*

(2) *The curves are all to be homeomorphic images of the interval $0 \leqslant t \leqslant 1$, and each curve is to have exactly one point on B, namely that of parameter $t = 0$. Each point of B is to be on at least one curve of F.*

(3) *The parameter value $t(p)$ on the curve of F through p (the curve may not be unique for $p \in B$, but then $t(p) = 0$) is to be a continuous function on A.*

(4) *For any $p \in A$ let U be a given neighbourhood of p and let q be a point such that p, q lie on some curve of F with $t(q) \geqslant t(p)$. Then there is a neighbourhood W of q and a number δ such that if p' is on a curve of F through W and if $\left|t(p') - t(p)\right| < \delta$, then $p' \in U$.*

Then under these conditions there is a homotopy of the identity

map of A on itself into a mapping which carries the set for which
$t(p) \leqslant \frac{1}{2}$ *onto B, while leaving those points for which* $t(p) = 1$
fixed.

The idea behind this lemma is, of course, that the part of each curve of F from $t = 0$ to $t = \frac{1}{2}$ is to be shrunk to the point $t = 0$ on B while the portion $t = \frac{1}{2}$ to $t = 1$ is stretched out. The proof consists of a straightforward verification that such an operation can be carried out, and that it represents a continuous mapping of $A \times I \to A$ as required.

The Shrinking Lemma will now be used to show that a neighbourhood of P in V can be retracted onto P in such a way that, if a point is on $V(z)$ for some $(z) \in L_0$ then throughout the retraction it remains in that same section $V(z)$. To verify this, construct in each section $V(z)$ geodesic arcs normal to P in a neighbourhood of P, that is to say geodesic with respect to the metric induced in $V(z)$ by the metric already selected on V. This is assumed to be done for each $(z) \in L_0$, remembering that there are no singularities on any of the $V(z)$ in a small enough neighbourhood of P. A compactness argument shows that the family of arcs F so constructed of length σ, say, for sufficiently small σ, entirely fills a neighbourhood $P(\sigma)$ of P. This is proved by noting that the equations of the curves of F depend analytically, not only of the initial conditions in each $V(z)$, but also on the real and imaginary parts of the coordinates of (z) on L_0. This same point implies by an easy deduction that the family F just defined can be used for the Shrinking Lemma with A and B replaced by $P(\sigma)$ and P respectively. The curves F are, of course, parametrized by arc-length from P. Summing up the result just obtained:

THEOREM 6. *There is a homotopy of the identity map of $P(\sigma)$ onto itself into a mapping of $P(\sigma)$ onto itself carrying $P(\sigma/2)$ into P, and leaving fixed the points at distance σ from P. Also if $\phi : P(\sigma) \times I \to P(\sigma)$ denotes the homotopy, I being the interval $0 \leqslant t \leqslant 1$, then $p \in V(z)$ implies $\phi(p, t) \in V(z)$ for all $t \in I$.*

The first application of this theorem is to the proof of an

excision theorem for sets of the type $V(A)$ where A is a subset of L_0. For the purpose of the following theorem it is not assumed that all the points of A are ordinary.

THEOREM 7. *Let A, B, C be three sets on L_0 such that $A \supset B \supset C$ and such that $\bar{C}$ is contained in the interior of B in the relative topology of A. Then the inclusion mapping $(V(A - C), V(B - C)) \to (V(A), V(B))$ induces isomorphisms of the corresponding homology groups.*

PROOF. Define $A' = V(A)$, $B' = V(B) \cup (A' \cap P(\sigma/2))$, $C' = V(C)$, where $P(\sigma/2)$ is as in Theorem 6. By the excision theorem for singular homology groups,

$$H_q(A', B') \cong H_q(A' - C', B' - C')$$

for each q. But, using Theorem 6, it turns out that the pair $(V(A), V(B))$ is a deformation retract of (A', B') and $(V(A-C), V(B - C))$ is a deformation retract of $(A' - C', B' - C')$, whence the required result follows.

A second application of Theorem 6 will now be given, of immediate importance in comparing homology groups associated with $V(K)$ and $X(K)$, where K is a set on L_0 consisting entirely of ordinary points. The mapping ψ of Theorem 4 is a relative homeomorphism of the pair $(X(K), X'(K))$ onto the pair $(V(K), P)$, that is to say induces a homeomorphism of $X(K) - X'(K)$ onto $V(K) - P$. Now, in general, the singular homology groups are not invariant under relative homeomorphisms. That is to say, it is not a priori evident that $H_q(X(K), X'(K)) \cong H_q(V(K), P)$ for all q. In this case, however, this isomorphism does hold, as will be shown by proving that ψ is a relative homeomorphism of a special kind, to be described in the following lemma.

LEMMA. *Let A, B, C, D be four spaces, $B \subset A$, $D \subset C$ and let $f : A \to C$ be a mapping which induces a homeomorphism of $A - B$ onto $C - D$. Let U be a neighbourhood of B in A, $W = f(U)$ a neighbourhood of D in C such that $\bar{B} \subset U$, $\bar{D} \subset W$. Finally suppose there is a homotopy of the identity map of the pair (A, U) onto itself into a mapping which carries U into B and still acts as the identity on B, and a similar homotopy with*

A, B, U, replaced by C, D, W. Then f induces an isomorphism $H_q(A, B) \cong H_q(C, D)$ for all q.

PROOF. This is a simple consequence of well known properties of homology groups, namely:

$H_q(A, B) \cong H_q(A, U)$ (Homotopy theorem)

$\cong H_q(A - B, U - B)$ (Excision theorem)

$\cong H_q(C - D, W - D)$ (isomorphism induced by f)

$\cong H_q(C, D)$ (reasoning as before).

The lemma just proved will now be applied to the comparison of $X(K)$ and $V(K)$.

THEOREM 8. Let K be a set of ordinary points of L_0. Then

$$H_q(V(K), P) \cong H_q(X(K), X'(K)),$$

for all q.

PROOF. To prove this, replace A, B, C, D, f of the above lemma by $X(K)$, $X'(K)$, $V(K)$, P, ψ respectively, ψ being the mapping of Theorem 4. The neighbourhood W of the above lemma is to be replaced by $P(\sigma/2)$ in the notation of Theorem 6, for suitable σ, while U is to be replaced by the full inverse image under ψ of W. There are two homotopies just as required in the lemma. That concerning W has been established by Theorem 6 (the mappings of that theorem being extended to act as the identity outside $P(\sigma)$), while that concerning U and $X(K)$ is obtained in a similar way by applying the Shrinking Lemma to the pair $(\overset{-1}{\psi} P(\sigma), X'(K))$, noting that the family of curves constructed in $P(\sigma)$ for the purpose of proving Theorem 6 is carried over into a suitable family of curves in the neighbourhood of $X'(K)$. Then the required result follows at once from the lemma.

The result of Theorem 8 is not general enough for future use, but will now be extended to a comparison of $H_q(V(K), V(M))$ and $H_q(X(K), X(M) \cup X'(K))$ where M is a subset of K. It will be shown that, under suitable conditions, these groups are isomorphic.

THEOREM 9. *Let M, U, K be three sets on L_0, K consisting of ordinary points, such that $M \subset U \subset K$. Let M be closed in K, U a neighbourhood of M in K and suppose that M is a deformation retract of U. Then*

$$H_q(V(M),\ P) \cong H_q(X(M) \cup X'(K),\ X'(K))$$

for all q.

PROOF. By the excision property of the relative homology groups

$$H_q(X(M) \cup X'(K),\ X'(K)) \cong H_q(X(M) \cup X'(U),\ X'(U))$$

for all q, the excised set being $X'(K - U) = P \times (K - U)$. By the hypotheses of the theorem there is a deformation retraction of U onto M, which extends to a retraction of $X'(U)$ onto $X'(M)$. Using Theorem 8 the result follows at once.

And now the result indicated before Theorem 9 will be obtained, by examining the diagrams I and II on p. 22, where the pairs $z_0 \in M$, $z_0 \in K$, $M \subset K$ all fulfil the conditions imposed on the pair $M \subset K$ in Theorem 9. The rows and columns are all exact sequences and commutativity holds throughout both diagrams. V_0 is written for $V(z_0)$.

THEOREM 10. *The two diagrams I, II are isomorphic under mappings induced by the mapping ψ of Theorem 4.*

PROOF. The three pairs $z_0 \in M$, $z_0 \in K$, $M \subset K$ are all suitable for the application of Theorem 9, and so, by that theorem,

$$H_q(X,\ X'(K)) \cong H_q(W,\ P)$$

for all q, where X can be $V_0 \cup X'(K)$, $X(M) \cup X'(K)$ or $X(K)$ and W is, respectively, V_0, $V(M)$ or $V(K)$. When all these isomorphisms are set up, an application of the "five lemma" (cf. [4]) shows that the diagrams are isomorphic.

COROLLARY. *In particular, under the conditions on M and K in Theorem 9*

$$H_q(V(K),\ V(M)) \cong H_q(X(K),\ X(M) \cup X'(K))$$

or all q.

$$
\begin{array}{ccccccccc}
\to H_q(V_0 \cup X'(K), X'(K)) & \to & H_q(X(M) \cup X'(K), X'(K)) & \to & H_q(X(M) \cup X'(K), V_0 \cup X'(K)) & \to & H_{q-1}(V_0 \cup X'(K), X'(K)) \to \\
\downarrow & & \downarrow & & \downarrow & & \downarrow \\
\to H_q(V_0 \cup X'(K), X'(K)) & \to & H_q(X(K), X'(K)) & \to & H_q(X(K), V_0 \cup X'(K)) & \to & H_{q-1}(V_0 \cup X'(K), X'(K)) \to \\
\downarrow & & \downarrow & & \downarrow & & \downarrow \\
\to 0 & \to & H_q(X(K), X(M) \cup X'(K)) & \to & H_q(X(K), X(M) \cup X'(K)) & \to & 0 \to \\
\downarrow & & \downarrow & & \downarrow & & \downarrow \\
\to H_{q-1}(V_0 \cup X'(K), X'(K)) & \to & H_{q-1}(X(M) \cup X'(K), X'(K)) & \to & H_{q-1}(X(M) \cup X'(K), V_0 \cup X'(K)) & \to & H_{q-2}(V_0 \cup X'(K), X'(K)) \to \\
\downarrow & & \downarrow & & \downarrow & & \downarrow
\end{array}
$$

Diagram I

$$
\begin{array}{ccccccccc}
\to H_q(V_0, P) & \to & H_q(V(M), P) & \to & H_q(V(M), V_0) & \to & H_{q-1}(V_0, P) \to \\
\downarrow & & \downarrow & & \downarrow & & \downarrow \\
\to H_q(V_0, P) & \to & H_q(V(K), P) & \to & H_q(V(K), V_0) & \to & H_{q-1}(V_0, P) \to \\
\downarrow & & \downarrow & & \downarrow & & \downarrow \\
\to 0 & \to & H_q(V(K), V(M)) & \to & H_q(V(K), V(M)) & \to & 0 \to \\
\downarrow & & \downarrow & & \downarrow & & \downarrow \\
\to H_{q-1}(V_0, P) & \to & H_{q-1}(V(M), P) & \to & H_{q-1}(V(M), V_0) & \to & H_{q-2}(V_0, P) \to \\
\downarrow & & \downarrow & & \downarrow & & \downarrow
\end{array}
$$

Diagram II

CHAPTER II

THE SINGULAR SECTIONS

1. Statement of the results

The object of this chapter is to study a set of the type $V(K)$, where K may now contain special points. $V(K)$ will be even less like a fibre bundle than in the case where K is restricted to consist of ordinary points, and in fact the covering homotopy theorem, Theorem 5, no longer holds. A special form of covering homotopy theorem holds in the situation now to be examined: namely, a retraction of K onto a subset containing the special points of K can be lifted to a retraction of $V(K)$. This chapter will be occupied mainly by the proof of this retraction theorem.

Let K then be a set on L_0 and let E be a subset of K such that all the points of $K - E$ are ordinary. Assume also that, if (z) is a special point belonging to E, $V(z)$ contains exactly one singularity. The last condition could be dispensed with, but is included because it makes some of the proofs easier and because this is the only case which will actually be used later. Finally it will be assumed that a family F of curves is given in K with the following properties:

(1) Each member of F is a homeomorphic image of the unit interval $0 \leqslant t \leqslant 1$ and the mapping of the interval into $K - E$ is real analytic for $t > 0$ (that is to say, real analytic in the sense of the real analytic structure of L_0). Also each curve of F is to have exactly one point on E, namely the point of parameter $t = 0$. Each point of E is to be on at least one curve of F.

(2) If $p \in K - E$, there is a neighbourhood U of p in which there is an admissible set of local coordinates (in the sense of the real analytic structure of L_0) of the form $(t, x_2, x_3, \ldots, x_{2n-2s})$, where t is as in (1), and the curves of F through U are, locally, the loci $x_2 = c_2, x_3 = c_3, \ldots, x_{2n-2s} = c_{2n-2s}$, where

23

the c_i are constants, a different set of constants belonging to each relevant curve.

Again stronger restrictions are being assumed than are necessary; the assumption of analyticity for the curves of F, rather than just differentiability is made to facilitate the proofs, and is in any case sufficient for later applications.

(3) The family F is to satisfy the conditions for the Shrinking Lemma, the sets A and B of that lemma being replaced by K and E.

It is clear, of course, that some of the Shrinking Lemma conditions are already implied by (1) and (2) above; (3) ensures that conditions (3) and (4) of the Shrinking Lemma are satisfied for $p \in E$.

The idea now is to show that the family F can be lifted into a similar family F' in $V(K)$ satisfying the conditions of the Shrinking Lemma with A and B replaced by $V(K) - P$ and $V(E) - P$. To construct the family F', consider any curve $\gamma \in F$. Let (ζ) be the point on γ of parameter $t = 0$, and let $C(\zeta)$ denote the singularity on $V(\zeta)$ if (ζ) is special. Then $V(\gamma) - P - C(\zeta)$ is a real analytic manifold and the $V(z)$ for $(z) \in \gamma$ form a family of submanifolds of which one passes through each point. Construct, in $V(\gamma) - P - C(\zeta)$, the orthogonal trajectories of this family of submanifolds. If this is carried out for each $\gamma \in F$, a family F' of analytic curves in $V(K)$ is obtained. Certain members of F' do not have points defined on them for $t = 0$, on account of the removal of singular points on sections $V(\zeta)$ for (ζ) special. When this defect has been remedied, as it will be in the course of the proof of Lemma c of §2, F' will satisfy the Shrinking Lemma conditions as already indicated. More explicitly, the following theorem will be proved:

THEOREM 11. (1) *The Shrinking Lemma holds for the family F', with A, B replaced by $V(K) - P$, $V(E) - P$, respectively.*

(2) *If $p \in P$, and U is a given neighbourhood of p, there is a neighbourhood U' of p such that any curve of F' meeting U' lies entirely in U.*

The proof of this will be postponed for a moment. In the meantime, an immediate consequence of Theorem 11 is:

THEOREM 12. *Let K and E be as above; let $K_0 \subset K$ be the subset for which $t = 1$ (t being the parameter on curves of F) and let K_1 be the set for which $t \leqslant \frac{1}{2}$. Then there is a homotopy of the identity mapping of $V(K)$ onto itself into a mapping which acts as identity on $V(K_0)$ and carries $V(K_1)$ onto $V(E)$. Points of $V(E)$ are fixed throughout the deformation.*

PROOF. By the first part of Theorem 11 along with the Shrinking Lemma there is a mapping $\phi : (V(K) - P) \times I \to V(K) - P$, where I is the unit interval $0 \leqslant s \leqslant 1$, such that $\phi(p, 1) = p$, all p, and $\phi(p, 0) = p$ for $p \in V(K_0) - P$, and $\phi(p, 0) \in V(E)$ for $p \in V(K_1) - P$. Now extend ϕ to points of $P \times I$ by setting $\phi(p, s) = p$ for all $p \in P$ and $s \in I$. Part (2) of Theorem 11 implies at once that the extended mapping ϕ is continuous on $V(K) \times I$, and so ϕ effects the required homotopy.

Theorem 12 is the main result of this chapter; roughly speaking it says that Shrinking Lemma conditions in the pair K, E can be lifted to similar conditions in $V(K)$, $V(E)$, and this is the restricted form of the covering homotopy theorem which holds when singular sections of V are involved. The remainder of the chapter will be occupied with the analytical details of the proof of Theorem 11.

2. Proof of Theorem 11

The proof of the second part of Theorem 11, which is a rather elaborate computation, will be tackled first. To begin with, some special coordinate systems will be set up. Let $q \in P$, and let $(\xi) = (\xi_1, \xi_2, \ldots, \xi_{2r+2s-2n})$ be a set of local coordinates on $V(\zeta)$ around q, where the ξ_i vanish at q; here (ζ) is any point of L_0, ordinary or special. Next, set up coordinates (ξ, u), normal coordinates in a normal neighbourhood of q over a neighbourhood of q in $V(\zeta)$. In addition (cf. Lemma b, §3, Chapter I), around any point near q but not on P there is a local coordinate system of the type (ξ, x). By Lemma c, §3, Chapter I, $V(z)$ has locally the equations

$u_i = f_i(\xi, x)$, $i = 1, 2, \ldots, 2n - 2s$, and these same equations can be used to make the transition from the (ξ, u) system of coordinates to the (ξ, x) system.

Now at a point p near q but not on P, if $p \in V(z)$ and $(z) \in \gamma$, a curve belonging to the family F, the member of the family F' through p must be tangential to $V(\gamma)$ and orthogonal to $V(z)$. This condition implies that, in terms of coordinates (ξ, x) around p, the differential equations of the family F' can be written in the form:

$$\left(I \left(\frac{\partial f}{\partial \xi} \right)' \right) G \left(\begin{array}{c|c} I & 0 \\ \hline \dfrac{\partial f}{\partial \xi} & \dfrac{\partial f}{\partial x} \end{array} \right) \left(\begin{array}{c} \dfrac{d\xi}{dt} \\ \dfrac{dx}{dt} \end{array} \right) = 0 \tag{1}$$

$$dx_i/dt = d\phi_i/dt, \ i = 1, 2, \ldots, 2n - 2s,$$

where partitioned matrix notation is used; $\dfrac{\partial f}{\partial \xi}$ is the $(2n - 2s) \times (2r - 2n + 2s)$ matrix whose ij-th element is $\dfrac{\partial f_i}{\partial \xi_j}$ and $\left(\dfrac{\partial f}{\partial \xi} \right)'$ is its transpose, a similar notation being used in $\dfrac{\partial f}{\partial x}$; $\dfrac{d\xi}{dt}, \dfrac{dx}{dt}$ denote the columns of derivatives of the ξ_i and x_j with respect to t; the matrix G has as elements the coefficients g_{ij} of the Riemann metric on V with respect to the local coordinates (ξ, u); and finally $x_i = \phi_i(t)$, $i = 1, 2, \ldots, 2n - 2s$ are the equations of the curve γ of F.

Using the equations $u_i = f_i(\xi, x)$, the g_{ij} can be written as analytic functions of the ξ_i and x_j. The product of the first three matrices in (1) can then be written as a matrix H whose elements h_{ij} are analytic functions of the ξ_i and x_j. The values of the h_{ij} at q will now be calculated, the object being to show that, at points near enough to q, the equations (1) can be solved for the $d\xi_i/dt$ in terms of the dx_i/dt.

Now $V(\zeta)$ is defined by $u_i = 0$, $i = 1, 2, \ldots, 2n - 2s$. And so, setting $\zeta_j = \alpha_{2j-1} + i\alpha_{2j}$, it follows that the f_i vanish when the x_j are set equal to the corresponding α_j. On the other hand, if the ξ_i are put equal to 0, for any values of the x_j, the u_j will vanish. It follows that, when the f_h are written as power series in the ξ_i and $(x_j - \alpha_j)$, every term must contain as a factor $(x_i - \alpha_i)\xi_j$ for some i and j. The matrices $\dfrac{\partial f}{\partial \xi}$, $\dfrac{\partial f}{\partial x}$ are therefore both zero when $x_i - \alpha_i = 0$ $(i = 1, \ldots, 2n - 2s)$, $\xi_j = 0$ $(j = 1, \ldots, 2r - 2n + 2s)$, and so, for these values of the variables, H reduces to $(g \mid 0)$, in partitioned matrix notation, where g is the submatrix of G consisting of the g_{ij} with $i, j = 1, 2, \ldots, 2r - 2n + 2s$, these elements being evaluated at q. But since G is a positive definite matrix, this submatrix, being symmetrically situated, is non-singular. It follows at once that, when the ξ_i and the $x_j - \alpha_j$ are sufficiently small, H is of the form $(H_1 \mid H_2)$, in partitioned notation, where H_1 is non-singular. Hence the equations (1) can be solved, the solutions being of the form

$$\frac{d\xi_i}{dt} = \sum_{j=1}^{2n-2s} a_{ij} \frac{dx_j}{dt}, \; i = 1, 2, \ldots, 2r - 2n + 2s, \qquad (2)$$

where the a_{ij} are analytic functions of the ξ_i and x_j, these solutions being valid for the ξ_i and $(x_j - \alpha_j)$ sufficiently small.

Some further information on the a_{ij} is available. For, when the ξ_i are all zero, the matrix $\dfrac{\partial f}{\partial x}$ is zero, as has already been pointed out. And when this happens, the last $2n - 2s$ columns of H are zero. It follows that, when the ξ_i are all zero, the a_{ij} vanish.

The phrase "sufficiently small" as applied to the ξ_i and $x_j - \alpha_j$ requires explanation at this point. The starting point of this working was a set of normal coordinates in a normal neighbourhood over a neighbourhood in $V(\zeta)$. Points at which equations (1) or their solutions (2) make sense must therefore lie in a neighbourhood U_ζ of q, which can be assumed to be a normal neighbourhood. Suitable selection of U_ζ will make the ξ_i sufficiently small for the solutions (2) to hold. In addition, the points in question can be represented in a coordinate system (ξ, x), where a point with the coordinates (ξ, x) lies in $V(z)$, the x_i being the real and imaginary parts of the z_j. Thus to make the $x_i - \alpha_i$ sufficiently small for (2) to hold, (z) must lie in a sufficiently small neighbourhood W_ζ of (ζ) on L_0.

Now when $(z) \in W_\zeta$, the functions dx_i/dt are bounded. And, since the a_{ij} are analytic for $(\xi, x) \in U_\zeta$, and $(z) \in W_\zeta$, and since these functions vanish for $\xi_i = 0$, $i = 1, 2, \ldots$, $2r - 2n + 2s$, it follows that the a_{ij} are bounded multiples of $\xi = \sum_1^{2r-2n+2s} |\xi_i|$ whenever $(\xi, x) \in U_\zeta$ and $(z) \in W_\zeta$. That is to say, there is a constant k_ζ such that, for $(\xi, x) \in U_\zeta$ and $(z) \in W_\zeta$,

$$\left| \frac{d\xi_i}{dt} \right| < k_\zeta \xi. \tag{3}$$

The next step is to transform the inequality (3) into a similar one, which however, does not depend on any particular coordinate system. Let $(y) = (y_1, y_2, \ldots, y_{2r})$ be normal coordinates on V around q. That is to say they are coordinates in terms of which the geodesic arcs through q have the equations $y_i = \lambda_i s$, where s is geodesic arc length from q, and the λ_i are fixed for each such arc. In addition, in terms of the y_i the geodesic distance squared from q, namely s^2, is a quadratic function of the y_i with constant coefficients.

On the other hand, at points of a curve satisfying the differential equations (1), s is a function of the parameter t. An upper bound for $\left(\dfrac{ds}{dt} \right) \Big/ s$ will now be obtained for points near q.

In the first place, the y_i can be written as power series in the local coordinates (ξ, u) around q, and since s^2 is a quadratic function of the y_i, it can be written as a power series in the ξ_i and u_j all of whose terms are of degree at least two. It follows that $2s(ds/dt)$ is a linear combination of the $d\xi_i/dt$ and the du_j/dt with coefficients vanishing at q. When these coefficients are expressed back in terms of the y_i they will therefore be bounded multiples of s in a neighbourhood of

q. In other words, in a suitable neighbourhood U_0 of q, ds/dt is a linear combination $\Sigma a_i(d\xi_i/dt) + \Sigma b_j(du_j/dt)$ where the a_i and b_j are bounded.

Assume now that the neighbourhood U_ζ for which (3) holds is in U_0. Then $|ds/dt| \leqslant \Sigma|a_i|\,|(d\xi_i/dt)| + \Sigma|b_j|\,|(du_j/dt)| < \Sigma|a_i|k_\zeta\xi + \Sigma|b_j|\,|(du_j/dt)|$. On the other hand $|(du_i/dt)| =$

$$\left| \Sigma \frac{\partial f_i}{\partial \xi_j} \frac{d\xi_j}{dt} + \Sigma \frac{\partial f_i}{\partial x_j} \frac{dx_j}{dt} \right| < \Sigma \left| \frac{\partial f_i}{\partial \xi_j} \right| k_\zeta\xi + \Sigma \left| \frac{\partial f_i}{\partial x_j} \right| \left| \frac{dx_j}{dt} \right|.$$

But the $\dfrac{\partial f_i}{\partial x_j}$ all vanish when the ξ_i are put equal to zero, and so in a neighbourhood of q they are bounded multiples of ξ. Combining all the inequalities just established it follows that, if $(\xi, x) \in U_\zeta$ and $(z) \in W_\zeta$ where U_ζ and W_ζ are suitable neighbourhoods of q and (ζ) respectively, then there is a constant k_ζ' such that

$$|ds/dt| < k_\zeta'\xi. \tag{4}$$

Finally, the ξ_i can be expressed as power series in the y_j in a sufficiently small neighbourhood of q, and it can be assumed that U_ζ is small enough for this purpose. It follows at once that, in U_ζ, ξ is less than some constant multiple of s. Combining this with (4) it follows that, for each $(\zeta) \in L_0$, there are neighbourhoods U_ζ of q and W_ζ of (ζ) and a constant k_ζ'' such that

$$|ds/dt| < k_\zeta''s,$$

where it is understood that s is expressed as a function of t along some curve of the family F', that is, some curve satisfying the differential equations (1).

But L_0 is compact, and so can be covered by a finite number of neighbourhoods of the type W_ζ. Then taking U as the intersection of the corresponding finite collection of U_ζ and k as the maximum of the corresponding finite collection of k_ζ'', the following lemma sums up the result which has been obtained:

LEMMA a. *Let q be a point of P and let s denote geodesic arc distance from q. Along a curve of F', s is to be expressed as a* *function of t. Then in a sufficiently small neighbourhood U of q, there is a constant k such that $|ds/dt| < ks$.*

The properties of the family F' will now be deduced from this lemma.

LEMMA b. (1) *If U is a neighbourhood of a point $q \in P$, there is a neighbourhood W of q such that any curve of F' meeting W lies entirely in U.*

(2) *No curve of F' has a limit point on P.*

PROOF. The first part is, of course, part (2) of Theorem 11. To prove this result integrate the inequality of Lemma a, namely, $-ks < ds/dt < ks$, obtaining

$$s(t_1)e^{-k(t_2-t_1)} < s(t_2) < s(t_1)e^{k(t_2-t_1)}, \tag{5}$$

where t_1 and t_2 are two values of the parameter t on some curve of F', $s(t_1)$ and $s(t_2)$ being the corresponding values of s, and where it is assumed that the whole arc t_1t_2 on the curve in question lies in a sufficiently small neighbourhood U_0 of q for Lemma a to apply. Assume for convenience that $U_0 \subset U$, and that U_0 is a geodesic sphere about q of radius ρ. Let W be the geodesic sphere about q of radius $\frac{1}{2}\rho e^{-k}$. Then, since $|t_2 - t_1| < 1$, the inequality (5) shows that, if the point of parameter t_1 on the curve of F' in question lies in W, then this curve cannot leave U_0, and so lies entirely in U.

Part (2) of this lemma is an immediate corollary of the first part. For suppose a curve λ in the family F' has the limit point $q \in P$. Let U be any neighbourhood of q. Then if W is constructed as in part (1) of this lemma, λ must have a point in W, since q is a limit point of λ, and so λ must lie in U. But it is not possible for a curve to lie in every preassigned neighbourhood of q, and so the lemma is proved.

This completes the proof of part (2) of Theorem 11, and it remains now to prove part (1), namely that the family F' satisfies the Shrinking Lemma conditions with A, B replaced by $V(K) - P$, $V(E) - P$. Condition (1) obviously holds. Condition (2) requires checking, the following lemma giving the required result:

LEMMA c. *Every member of F' is either a homeomorphic*

image of the unit interval $0 \leqslant t \leqslant 1$, *or can be made so by the addition of the singular point on* $V(\zeta)$ *for some special point* (ζ) *of* E. *When this adjustment has been made condition* (2) *of the Shrinking Lemma holds for* F' *with respect to* $V(K) - P$ *and* $V(E) - P$.

PROOF. Let C be the set of singular points on all the sections $V(z)$ for $(z) \in \Gamma$ in the notation of §2, Chapter I. It has already been assumed that, for $(z) \in \Gamma \cap K$, $V(z)$ has exactly one singular point $C(z)$. It is clear that the orthogonal trajectory construction makes sense on $V(K) - P - C$. That is to say, certain of the members of F', as already constructed, meet $V(E)$ at points not on C, and such curves are orthogonal trajectories right up to $t = 0$. Call the set of such curves F'_1 and let the remaining members of F' be called F'_2. The curves of F'_1 are analytically homeomorphic images of the interval $0 \leqslant t \leqslant 1$. On the other hand, a curve γ' of F'_2 must lie in a set $V(\gamma)$, where γ is a curve of F ending (for $t = 0$) at a point $(\zeta) \in \Gamma \cap K$ and it is clear that γ' must have some limit point on $V(\zeta)$. This limit point is not on P, by Lemma b above, and is not on $V(\zeta) - P - C(\zeta)$, since then γ' would be in F'_1. Hence as t tends to zero, the points of γ' tend to the unique point $C(\zeta)$. If $C(\zeta)$ is added to γ' this curve becomes a homeomorphic image (not necessarily analytic at $t = 0$) of the interval $0 \leqslant t \leqslant 1$. If all the curves of F'_2 are treated in this way, the required result is obtained, namely that every curve of F' is a homeomorphic image of $0 \leqslant t \leqslant 1$. The fact that every curve of F' has exactly one point on $V(E) - P$ follows from the corresponding property of the family F. A point $p \in V(\zeta)$ for (ζ) in E is clearly the end point of a member of F' if (ζ) is ordinary or if (ζ) is special and p is non-singular on $V(\zeta)$. Suppose that, for (ζ) special, the point $C(\zeta)$ is not the end point of any curve of F'. It would then follow that $V(z)$ for (z) on a curve of F ending at (ζ) would be homeomorphic to $V(\zeta) - C(\zeta)$, but this is impossible since $V(z)$ is compact and $V(\zeta) - C(\zeta)$ is not. This completes the verification of condition (2) of the Shrinking Lemma.

Condition (3) of the Shrinking Lemma for F' follows easily from the corresponding condition for F. Condition (4) will be shown to hold by means of the following three lemmas.

LEMMA d. *Let p be any point of $V(K) - P - C$, where C is as in the proof of the last lemma. Let q be a point such that p, q lie on some curve of F' with $t(q) \geqslant t(p)$. Then for any given neighbourhood U of p there is a neighbourhood W of q and a number δ such that if p' is on a curve of F' meeting W and $|t(p') - t(p)| < \delta$, then $p' \in U$.*

PROOF. This is simply a statement of the properties of the integral curves of a set of ordinary differential equations of the first order and degree.

This lemma checks condition (4) of the Shrinking Lemma for F' except when $p \in C$. This case will now be dealt with in two stages.

LEMMA e. *Define the mapping $f : V(K) \to V(E)$ as follows:*

$f(p) = p$ *if $p \in P$; otherwise $f(p)$ is the end point on $V(E)$ of any curve of F' through p (this curve only fails to be unique if $p \in C$ and then the definition gives $f(p) = p$ unambiguously). Then f is a continuous mapping.*

PROOF. Note first that Lemmas c and d imply the continuity of f at any point p such that $f(p) \notin C$. Let $f(p) = q \in C$; it is required to prove that f is continuous at p. Let Φ be the filter of neighbourhoods of p in $V(K)$. $f(\Phi)$ is the basis of a filter on V. (Bourbaki [1], p. 40.) V is compact and so $f(\Phi)$ has an adherent point q'. If $p \in V(z)$, $q \in V(\zeta)$ it is not hard to see that, by projecting the family F' onto the family F, f induces a mapping $f_0 : K \to E$ such that $f_0(z) = (\zeta)$. On account of the given properties of F, the mapping f_0 is continuous. It is then not hard to see that $q' \in V(\zeta)$. The next step is to show that $q' = q = C(\zeta)$, the singular point of $V(\zeta)$. Suppose that $q' \neq C(\zeta)$. If $q' \in P$ there are neighbourhoods U_1 and U_2 of p and q' such that $U_1 \cap U_2 = \emptyset$ (for $p \notin P$). Then, by Lemma b of this section, there is a neighbourhood U_3 of q' such that every curve of F' meeting U_3 lies entirely in U_2. Hence $f^{-1}(U_3) \cap U_1 = \emptyset$. If on the other hand $q' \notin P$, still assuming that $q' \neq C(\zeta)$, the properties of the differential equations of F', depending analytically on the local coordinates, imply that $\overset{-1}{f}(q')$ is a compact set in $V(K)$ not containing p. And a simple argument shows that there are neighbourhoods U_1 of p and U_3 of q' such that $\overset{-1}{f}(U_3) \cap U_1 = \emptyset$. But $U_1 \in \Phi$ and so q' is adherent to $f(U_1)$ and so $f(U_1) \cap U_3$ contains a point $q'' = f(p')$, $p' \in U_1$. Thus $p' \in \overset{-1}{f}(U_3) \cap U_1$. This contradiction shows that $q' \neq C(\zeta)$ is impossible. Hence $f(\Phi)$ has a unique adherent point $C(\zeta) = q$, and so f is continuous at p (Bourbaki [1], p. 92 and p. 52). This completes the proof of the lemma.

LEMMA f. *Let U be a neighbourhood of $C(\zeta) \in C$ and let q be some point on a curve of F' ending at $C(\zeta)$. Then there is a neighbourhood W of q and a number $\delta > 0$ such that if a point p' lies on a curve of F' through W and $t(p') < \delta$, then $p' \in U$.*

PROOF. Let U' be a second neighbourhood of $C(\zeta)$ such that $\bar{U}' \subset U$. Then by the last lemma, there is a neighbourhood W of q such that all curves of F' meeting W end in U'. Suppose now that, for every number δ, there is some curve of F' through W containing a point of parameter $<\delta$ outside U; that is, suppose that the present lemma is false. Then it may be assumed, since the curve in question ends in U', that for each δ there is a point $p(\delta)$ of parameter $<\delta$ lying on the frontier of U. As δ tends to zero the points $p(\delta)$ will have some limit point p_0 on the frontier of U, and so not in P if U has been taken small enough to begin with. Of course $p_0 \in V(E)$. Take a neighbourhood U_1 of p_0 such that $U_1 \cap U' = \emptyset$. Then if U_2 is any neighbourhood of p_0, there are curves of F' through U_2 and ending in U', namely curves containing points $p(\delta)$ for δ small enough; whereas, by Lemma e above it should be possible to choose U_2 so that all curves of F' meeting it end in U_1. This contradiction proves Lemma f.

The verification of condition (4) of the Shrinking Lemma for F' is thus completed, and so Theorems 11 and 12 are completely proved.

CHAPTER III

A PENCIL OF
HYPERPLANE SECTIONS

1. The choice of a pencil

The present chapter will be concerned with preparing the way for the inductive proof of the theorems whose statements were indicated in the introduction. The idea will be to discuss the homology of V modulo V_0, where V_0 is a hyperplane section of V, by taking V_0 as a member of a pencil of hyperplane sections of V. The induction hypotheses will then be applied to a pencil of hyperplane sections of V_0, that is sections of V by linear $(n-2)$-spaces. The choice of a hyperplane pencil for this purpose requires a little care to ensure that the induction hypotheses which are to be made carry over properly from one dimension to the next. The way of making this choice will be the subject of this first section.

Let L be a generic $(n-3)$-space in L^n. By Theorem 1, the set of $(n-2)$-spaces through L cutting singular sections on the non-singular variety V in L^n is a one-dimensional algebraic family whose generic member cuts a section with exactly one singular point. If L_0 is a plane not meeting L, the family Λ of $(n-2)$-spaces through L can be parametrized by the points of L_0 (cf. §2, Chapter I). Those points of L_0 corresponding to $(n-2)$-spaces cutting singular sections form a curve Γ on L_0. Also if C is the set of all points of V each of which occurs as a singular point on some section of V by an $(n-2)$-space through L, then C is a curve projecting on Γ from L.

The following lemmas can easily be verified by inspection of V and of the section of its dual V' by the plane dual to L. It will be assumed for the remainder of this section that V' is of dimension $n-1$, so that its section by the dual of L is a curve.

LEMMA a. *Through L there is just a finite number of hyperplanes whose sections with V have singularities at singular points of C.*

LEMMA b. *There is at most a finite number of hyperplanes through L having triple contacts with C.*

LEMMA c. *There is at most a finite number of points Q_1, $Q_2, \ldots, Q_p$ on C such that the tangent to C at Q_i meets L.*

The above lemmas will now be applied to the operation of choosing a pencil Π of hyperplanes suitable for the purpose of this monograph. Let π be the plane in L'^n dual to L, and let Σ be the finite set of points on π consisting of the following:

(1) Points corresponding to hyperplanes of L^n through L and containing the tangent linear variety to V at some singularity of C (Lemma a).

(2) Points corresponding to hyperplanes through L having triple intersections with C (Lemma b).

(3) Points on π corresponding to hyperplanes of L^n containing the tangent linear variety to V at one of the points $Q_1, Q_2, \ldots, Q_p$ of Lemma c. There can only be a finite number of such points, since otherwise the section of V' by π would have a line as component, which cannot happen since V' is irreducible and is not a hyperplane.

(4) The intersections of π with the singular locus of V'. There will only be a finite number of these since this locus has dimension $\leqslant n - 2$.

Let L_1 be a generic $(n - 2)$-space through L in L^n. Then it does not meet C and the line l in π corresponding to it by duality does not contain any of the points of Σ as listed above. Let Π be the pencil of hyperplanes in L^n with the axis L_1. The hyperplanes of Π are parametrized by a single complex variable z, admitting the value ∞, that is by the points of a complex projective line (topologically the Riemann sphere of complex variable theory) and the section of V by the hyperplane $\Pi(z)$ of parameter z will be called $V(z)$. Note that this is the notation of §2, Chapter I, with L, Λ, L_0 replaced by L_1, Π and a complex line. Then Π has the following properties:

THEOREM 13. **(a)** *The pencil* Π *has at most a finite number of hyperplanes cutting singular sections on* V, *and each such section has exactly one singular point. The finite set of singular points* C_1, C_2, ..., C_k *has no member on* $V \cap L_1$.

(b) *If* $\Pi(z)$ *is any hyperplane of* Π *cutting a non-singular section* $V(z)$ *on* V, *then the set of linear* $(n - 2)$-*spaces through* L *in* $\Pi(z)$ *cuts a pencil of sections on* $V(z)$ *only a finite number of which have singularities. For generic* z, *and so with only a finite number of exceptions, each of these singular sections of* $V(z)$ *will have exactly one singular point, and this point will not lie on* L.

(c) C_i *being the singular point on the singular section* $V(z_i)$ *by a hyperplane of* Π, C_i *is a simple point of* C *and the tangent to* C *at* C_i *lies in* $\Pi(z_i)$ *and does not meet* L.

(d) $\Pi(z_i)$ *has a double intersection with* C *at* C_i.

(e) *There exists through each* C_i *a hyperplane containing* L *which cuts a non-singular section on* V.

PROOF. Most of this theorem is a consequence of the fact that the line l corresponding by duality to the axis of Π does not pass through the points of Σ listed above under (1) . . . (4). The inclusion of the set (4) in Σ implies (a) in the present theorem (cf. proof of Lemma c, §1, Chapter I). (b) follows from Theorem 1 and the fact that the $(n - 2)$-spaces through L and lying in a generic hyperplane through L correspond to a generic line on L_0, which meets the curve Γ in a finite number of points, each generic on Γ. (c) follows from the inclusion of (1) and (3) in Σ, and (d) from the inclusion of (2) in Σ. (e) can easily be verified directly.

A pencil Π satisfying the conditions of Theorem 13 would not be quite good enough for the subsequent working, as an inductive argument is to be carried out. It is, however, a matter of routine verifications to see the following:

THEOREM 14. *Let* H_1, H_2, ..., H_n *be* n *independent hyperplanes in* L^n. *Then the pencil* Π_1 *of axis* $H_1 \cap H_2$ *satisfies the requirements of Theorem 13, taking* $H_1 \cap H_2 \cap H_3$ *as* L. *In any hyperplane of* Π_1, *with a finite number of exceptions, Theorem 13 holds for the pencil* Π_2 *of* $(n - 2)$-*spaces with axis* $H_1 \cap H_2 \cap H_3$, *the linear space* $H_1 \cap H_2 \cap H_3 \cap H_4$ *being taken as L. In any member of* Π_2, *with a finite number of exceptions, Theorem 13 holds for the pencil* Π_3 *of* $(n-3)$-*spaces with axis* $H_1 \cap H_2 \cap H_3 \cap H_4$, $H_1 \cap H_2 \cap H_3 \cap H_4 \cap H_5$ *acting as L, and so on step by step.*

In addition $H_1, \ldots, H_n$ may be specialized to hyperplanes whose equations have complex coefficients, and, provided that these coefficients fail to satisfy a finite number of polynomial equations, Theorem 14 will still hold.

It will be understood in future that the pencil Π has the properties of a specialization of Π_1 of this type with L as the $(n-3)$-space $H_1 \cap H_2 \cap H_3$. In Chapter VII a further condition will be imposed on Π, but it is more convenient to postpone the statement of it until it is actually needed.

2. Notation

In this section some notational conventions will be set up which will hold for the rest of the work.

As above, V will be a non-singular r-dimensional algebraic variety over the complex numbers in the projective n-space L^n. No assumption will, however, be made as to the dimension of its dual V'. At various points in the subsequent arguments the two cases dim $V' = n-1$ and dim $V' < n-1$ will have to be discussed separately.

Π will be a pencil of hyperplanes in L^n as in Theorem 14 with axis L_1, and L will be a linear $(n-3)$-space in L_1. Members of Π will be parametrized by points of a complex projective line S (i.e. a 2-sphere). The notation of §3, Chapter I, will be applied to the sections of V by members of Π. That is to say, $V(z)$ is the section of V by the hyperplane in Π with parameter z, and, if K is a set on S, $V(K)$ will denote $\bigcup V(z)$, the union being taken over all $z \in K$. In particular $V_0 = V(z_0)$ will denote some selected non-singular section of V. The values of z for which $V(z)$ has a singularity, namely the special points on S, will be denoted by $z_1, z_2, \ldots, z_k$.

On the other hand, the $(n-2)$-spaces through L form a family Λ as in §2, Chapter I, parametrized by the points of a plane L_0. It is not hard to see that affine coordinates (z, w) can be introduced on L_0 in such a way that z is the parameter of the pencil Π. When this is done, using the notation of §3, Chapter I, the section of V by the member of Λ corresponding to the point (z, w) of L_0 will be denoted by $V(z, w)$. Special points on L_0, as seen in Chapter I, form a curve Γ. It should be noted that the term "special point" generally needs the qualification "on S" or "on L_0," but the meaning will usually be clear in any given context.

A notation for sets of sections by members of Λ must be introduced to avoid confusion with sets of sections by members of Π. If H is a set of values of z and K is a set of values of w then $V(H, K)$ will denote $\cup V(z, w)$, the union being taken over all $z \in H$ and $w \in K$. This notation will not, of course, cover all possible sets in L_0, but it is sufficient for all the sets actually to be used in what follows. One particular section will be given a name of its own; namely $V \cap L_1$ will be denoted by P (this is the notation of §3, Chapter I, applied to the family Π rather than to Λ).

As in §1, above, C will denote the set of all singular points on all sections $V(z, w)$ with $(z, w) \in \Gamma$; C is a curve projecting on Γ from L. Points of C will generally be denoted by the letter C with subscripts, superscripts or primes attached, as was done, for example, in Theorem 13, where C_i denoted the singularity on $V(z_i)$.

It will often be convenient to regard the coordinate w on L_0 as the parameter of a second hyperplane pencil Π' in L^n. When this is done, the section of V by the hyperplane of parameter w in Π' will be denoted by $V'(w)$.

3. Reduction to local theorems

It will now be shown that one of the principal aims of this work, namely to study the homology groups $H_q(V, V_0)$, can be reduced to the consideration of neighbourhoods of the singular points on the singular sections $V(z_i)$, $i = 1, 2, \ldots, k$, of V by hyperplanes of the pencil Π. The first stage in this reduction is to apply the theory of Chapters I and II to the fibring of V by the sections cut by Π. In this section it is assumed that the dual of V is of dimension $n - 1$, so that there are singular sections by hyperplanes of Π.

Let K be a set on S which is either the whole of S or is a closed disc on S containing the special points $z_1, z_2, \ldots, z_h$ in its interior and no special point on its circumference. Assume also that the ordinary point z_0 is an interior point of K. Let λ_i be an arc in K joining z_0 and z_i $(i = 1, 2, \ldots, h)$, λ_i being analytically homeomorphic to a closed line interval and no two of the λ_j having any point except z_0 in common. Let K_0 denote the point-set union of the λ_i. Cover K by means of two closed sets U_0 and U, where U_0 is a neighbourhood of K_0 and $K_0 \cap U = \emptyset$; a simple way to do this is to take U_0 as the union of closed circles of some fixed radius with centres at all points of K_0 and U as the complement of a similar union of open circles of smaller radius. Applying Theorem 7 to the present situation, the following result is at once obtained:

LEMMA a. $H_q(V(K), V(U_0)) \cong H_q(V(U), V(U_0 \cap U))$, for all q.

An immediate consequence of this is:

LEMMA b. If $H_{q-2}(V_0, P)$ is zero, then $H_q(V(K), V(U_0))$ is zero.

PROOF. For, by the corollary to Theorem 10,

$$H_q(V(U), V(U_0 \cap U)) \cong H_q(X(U), X(U_0 \cap U) \cup X'(U))$$

for all q. Now if K is not the whole sphere S, U is homeomorphic to an annulus and $U_0 \cap U$ to a narrower annulus round the rim of U, and a fairly trivial sequence of retraction operations shows that $H_q(X(U), X(U_0 \cap U) \cup X'(U))$ is zero for all q. On the other hand, if $K = S$, U is a circular disc with $U_0 \cap U$ an annulus running round its circumference. In this case it is not hard to see that $H_q(X(U), X(U_0 \cap U) \cup X'(U)) \cong H_{q-2}(V_0, P)$, for one is essentially dealing here with a fibre space which is a product $V_0 \times U$. Thus if it is known that $H_{q-2}(V_0, P)$ is zero, $H_q(X(U), X(U_0 \cap U) \cup X'(U))$ will be zero. Combining these results with Lemma a, the present lemma follows.

The next lemma is derived from Lemma b by shrinking the neighbourhood U_0 onto K_0. In fact, if U_1 is a neighbourhood of K_0 similar to U_0 but containing it, it is not hard to see that a family of curves can be constructed in U_1 having the properties of the family F introduced at the beginning of Chapter II with the sets K and E of that section replaced here by U_1 and K_0. It follows at once (Theorem 12) that there is a homotopy of the identity mapping of $V(U_1)$ on itself into a mapping of $V(U_1)$ onto itself which carries $V(U_0)$ onto $V(K_0)$. The points of $V(K_0)$ are fixed throughout the deformation. Moreover it is easy to see that the homotopy may be extended to the whole of $V(K)$ by leaving all points of $V(K)$ outside $V(U_1)$ fixed. Combining this result with Lemma b, the following result is obtained:

LEMMA c. *If* $H_{q-2}(V, P) = 0$, *then* $H_q(V(K), V(K_0)) = 0$.

The main result of this section is the following theorem:

THEOREM 15. *If* $H_{q-2}(V_0, P) = 0$, $H_q(V(K), V_0)$ *is generated by the injection images of the groups* $H_q(V(\lambda_i), V_0)$, $i = 1$, $2, \ldots, h$.

PROOF. By Lemma c and the exactness of the homology sequence, $H_{q-2}(V_0, P) = 0$ implies that $H_q(V(K), V_0)$ is generated by the injection image of $H_q(V(K_0), V_0)$. Write $\lambda_i' = \lambda_i \cup (W \cap K_0)$, where W is a small closed neighbourhood of z_0. Then Theorem 7 along with the direct sum theorem of relative homology (Eilenberg and Steenrod [4] p. 33) implies $H_q(V(K_0), \bigcap_i V(\lambda_i')) = \Sigma_j H_q(V(\lambda_j'), \bigcap_i V(\lambda_i'))$. Finally an application of Theorem 5 to the retraction of $\bigcap \lambda_i'$ onto z_0 yields the result $H_q(V(K_0), V_0) = \Sigma H_q(V(\lambda_j), V_0)$, and this completes the theorem.

Now, in studying any one of the groups $H_q(V(\lambda_i), V_0)$ or its injection image, it is clear that z_0 may be assumed to be arbitrarily close to z_i, the corresponding λ_i being shrunk and Theorem 5 being applied to obtain a corresponding shrinkage of $V(\lambda_i)$. In considering one of these groups it is convenient to drop the suffix i. The notation used for such a situation will be as follows:

Let z' be a special point on S and let C' be the singular point on $V(z')$. z_0 is to be an ordinary point near z' and λ an analytic arc joining z_0 and z' on S.

It will now be shown that, in order to study the group $H_q(V(\lambda), V_0)$, it is only necessary to examine relative cycles on an arbitrarily small neighbourhood of C', provided that

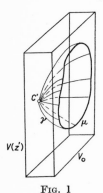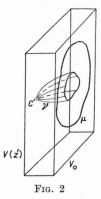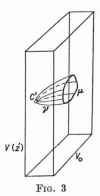

FIG. 1	FIG. 2	FIG. 3

z_0 is sufficiently near to z'. The idea involved here is illustrated in the accompanying diagrams. Let γ represent pictorially a relative q-cycle of $V(\lambda)$ modulo V_0, with boundary μ, say. In Fig. 1, γ is drawn 2-dimensional, and the rectangular slab denotes $V(\lambda)$, its left and right hand faces $V(z')$ and V_0 respectively. Constructing in $V(\lambda)$ orthogonal trajectories to the $V(z)$ for $z \in \lambda$, a family F of curves is obtained, one through each point of $V(\lambda)$ except C'. And so γ can be pulled back along the curves F except around the singular point C'. γ now takes the "broad-brimmed hat" shape of Fig. 2. Finally an excision argument shows that the brim may be more or less removed, so that γ is reduced to a chain on a neighbourhood of C' (cf. Fig. 3).

The argument just sketched will now be formulated properly.

THEOREM 16. *Let U be a preassigned neighbourhood of C'. Then, if λ is contained in a sufficiently small neighbourhood of z' on S, there is a set W contained in U such that the inclusion mapping $(W, W \cap V_0) \to (V(\lambda), V_0)$ induces isomorphisms onto of the corresponding homology groups.*

4

PROOF. Let U_1 and U_2 be two geodesic spheres about C' of radii ρ_1 and ρ_2 respectively with $\rho_1 < \rho_2$. If F is the family of orthogonal trajectories of the $V(z)$ in $V(\lambda)$, define the set W_0 as follows: W_0 is the union of all points lying on curves of F ending in U_1 along with the points of parameter t satisfying $(s - \rho_1)/(\rho_2 - \rho_1) \leqslant t \leqslant 1$ on curves of F ending at points of $V(z')$ at geodesic distance s from C' for all s such that $\rho_1 \leqslant s \leqslant \rho_2$. Lemma f, §2, Chapter II implies that, if U_1, U_2 are small enough and λ is contained in a small enough neighbourhood of z', then W_0 can be made to lie in the preassigned neighbourhood U of C' (it is assumed that the parameter t varies from 0 to 1 on curves of F). Next define W as the union of W_0 and a neighbourhood of $W_0 \cap V_0$ on V_0; it may be assumed that $W \subset U$. Then an application of the Shrinking Lemma using the curves F contained in $V(\lambda) - W_0$, along with an excision, gives the required result.

CHAPTER IV

LEFSCHETZ'S FIRST AND SECOND THEOREMS

1. Lefschetz's first main theorem

In this chapter the first two main theorems of the work will be stated and some consequences will be deduced. The proof of the first theorem will be given in detail, but that of the second, which is rather complicated, will be postponed to Chapter V. In the present chapter, however, a sketch of the ideas involved in proving the second main theorem will be given. And, in a similar way, the proof of the first theorem will be preceded by a geometrical description of the idea behind it.

The statement of the first main theorem, indicated in the introduction, is as follows:

THEOREM 17. *Let V be a non-singular algebraic variety of dimension r defined over the complex numbers and immersed in a projective space, and let V_0 be a non-singular hyperplane section. Then $H_q(V, V_0) = 0$ for $q \leq r - 1$.*

The first point to notice is that, if the theorem is true for one non-singular section V_0, it is true for any other V_1. For V_0 and V_1 can be taken as members of a pencil of hyperplane sections containing only a finite number of singular sections. The non-singular members of this pencil form a fibring of V in the sense described in Chapter I, and so, by Theorem 5, there is a homotopy of the identity mapping of V on itself into a mapping of V onto itself which carries V_0 onto V_1, and vice versa.

Then since Theorem 17 does not depend on the choice of the section V_0, it can be assumed that it is a member $V(z_0)$ of a pencil of sections cut by a hyperplane pencil Π with the properties described in Theorems 13 and 14.

The proof of Theorem 17 will actually be carried out by proving the following slightly more general theorem:

THEOREM 18. *Let V be a non-singular r-dimensional projective variety over the complex numbers, and Π a hyperplane pencil as in Theorem 14, the members of Π being parametrized by the points of the sphere (or complex projective line) S. Let K be a closed circular disc on S not having any special points z' on its boundary. Then $H_q(V(K), V_0) = 0$ for $q \leq r - 1$. In particular if K is taken as the whole sphere S, this reduces to Theorem 17.*

PROOF. This theorem will be proved by induction on r, and so it is assumed to start with that $H_q(V_0, P) = 0$ for $q \leq r - 2$. The theorem obviously holds for $r = 1$ which gives a basis for the induction.

The particular case in which there are no special points z_i on S (i.e. in which the dual of V is of dimension $< n - 1$) will be treated first. In this case, if $K \neq S$, the result is trivial, for V_0 is a deformation retract of $V(K)$ (by Theorem 5). To dispose of the case $K = S$, note first that Theorem 9 holds if the pair (K, M) is taken to be (S, z_0) and also that the conclusion of that theorem is trivial if $K = M = z_0$. Thus Theorem 10 holds if the triple (K, M, z_0) is taken to be (S, z_0, z_0), and yields the result $H_q(V, V_0) \cong H_q(X, V_0 \cup X')$. On the right of this isomorphism one is dealing with a fibre bundle over S as base, and a simple argument (either using the spectral sequence or by making a cellular decomposition of S) shows that $H_q(X, V_0 \cup X') \cong H_{q-2}(V_0, P) = 0$, by the induction hypothesis, and so $H_q(V, V_0) = 0$ for $q \leq r - 1$.

In the remainder of the proof of Theorem 18 it will be assumed that there are special points on S.

The induction hypothesis along with Theorem 15 shows that, for $q \leq r - 1$, $H_q(V(K), V_0)$ is generated by the injection images of the groups $H_q(V(\lambda_i), V_0)$, and so it simply has to be shown that these injection images are zero. Attention may therefore be confined to one of the $H_q(V(\lambda_i), V_0)$.

Changing notation as for Theorem 16, let z' be a special point on S, let C' be the singular point on $V(z')$ and let λ be an analytic arc joining z' to a nearby ordinary point z_0. Then it is sufficient, in order to complete the proof of Theorem 18, to show that, under the induction hypothesis, the image of the injection mapping $H_q(V(\lambda), V_0) \to H_q(V(K), V_0)$ is zero for $q \le r - 1$.

The proof of this statement is based on the following geometrical argument:

By Theorem 16, any element of $H_q(V(\lambda), V_0)$, if z_0 is sufficiently near z', can be represented by a relative cycle γ which is a chain on an arbitrarily preassigned neighbourhood of C'. The idea then is to show that γ must be homologous to zero, modulo V_0, in $V(K)$. To do this, introduce a second pencil Π' such that the section V_0' through C' cut by Π' is non-singular; this can be done by Theorem 13(e). If $q \le r - 1$, then $\mu = d\gamma$ is a cycle of dimension $\le r - 2$ on V_0 and so, by the induction hypothesis, is homologous to a cycle μ' on $V_0 \cap V_0'$, and, if γ has been made small enough, this homology can be carried out in a normal bundle over V_0'. Thus $\mu = \mu' + d\alpha$, and so $\gamma - \alpha$ is a relative cycle on $V(\lambda)$ modulo V_0, homologous to γ modulo V_0, lying in a normal bundle over V_0', and having its boundary in $V_0 \cap V_0'$. Using the projection in this normal bundle, $\gamma - \alpha$ may be flattened out into a relative cycle in V_0' modulo $V_0 \cap V_0'$. And finally a "rotation" of V_0' about $V_0 \cap V_0'$ pulls this flattened chain round into V_0. Hence γ is homologous to zero in V modulo V_0. It is finally shown by an excision argument that this homology can be carried out in $V(K)$.

The detailed proof of Theorem 18 will now be completed. As remarked above, it is only necessary to prove the following lemma.

LEMMA. *Under the induction hypothesis, and in the notation already introduced, the image of the injection homomorphism* $H_q(V(\lambda), V_0) \to H_q(V(K), V_0)$ *is zero for* $q \le r - 1$.

PROOF. Choose a pencil of hyperplanes Π' with the following properties:

(1) The section V_0' through C' cut by Π' is non-singular.

(2) If z is sufficiently close to z' the pencil Π cuts on $V(z)$ only a finite number of singular sections, each with one singular point (not lying on the axis of Π'). Also the axis of Π' meets $V(z)$ in a non-singular variety. Thus Π' bears the same sort of relation to $V(z)$ as Π bears to V.

(3) $V'_0 \cap V(z)$ is non-singular for z sufficiently near to z'. That such a pencil exists follows from Theorem 13. It is

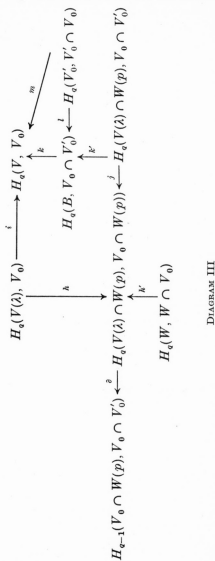

DIAGRAM III

clear that the coordinates (z, w) in L_0 can be chosen so that w is the parameter in the pencil Π'. It will be convenient to write $V'(w)$ for the section of V by the hyperplane of para-meter w in Π'.

Having chosen Π' with the stated properties, the following sequence of choices must be made:

(a) Construct a normal bundle B to V_0' in V.

(b) For any real number k, write $W(k)$ for the union of the $V'(w)$ such that $|w - w_0| \le k$, where w_0 is the parameter of V_0'. By Lemma d, §3, Chapter I, $W(k) \subset B$ if k is small enough. Choose the real numbers k,m such that $m < k$ and $W(m) \subset W(k) \subset B$.

(c) Around C' on V a set of local coordinates may be chosen to include the real and imaginary parts of w, since V_0' is non-singular, and so there is a neighbourhood U of C' such that $U \subset W(m)$.

(d) Construct W in Theorem 16 so that $W \subset U$.

(e) Choose a number p, $m < p \le k$, such that no section $V'(w) \cap V_0$ with $|w - w_0| = p$ is singular.

In Diagram III all the maps except ∂ are induced by the appropriate inclusions, and ∂ is the boundary homomorphism of the exact homology sequence of the triple

$$(V_0 \cap V_0', \ V_0 \cap W(p), \ V(\lambda) \cap W(p)),$$

part of which forms the horizontal line in the middle of the diagram.

It will now be shown that the image of i in Diagram III is zero. To prove this, note first that, by Theorem 16, hh' is onto and therefore so is h. Also, by the induction hypothesis $H_{q-1}(V_0 \cap W(p), V_0 \cap V_0') = 0$, and so the exactness of the homology sequence in the diagram implies that j is onto. It then follows at once from the commutativity of the square in the middle of the diagram that the image of i is contained in the image of kk', and so in the image of k. On the other hand, V_0' is a deformation retract of B, and so l is an isomorphism onto, which implies that the image of k is the same as the image of m. Thus the image of i is contained in that of m. But V_0, V_0' and $V_0 \cap V_0'$ are all non-singular, and so the hyperplanes cutting V_0 and V_0' determine a pencil Π'' cutting, like Π, only a finite number of singular sections on V. The sections of V by the hyperplanes of Π'' thus determine a "fibring" of V as described in Chapter I, and in particular, by Theorem 5, there is a homotopy of the inclusion $(V_0', V_0' \cap V_0) \to (V, V_0)$ into a mapping whose image lies entirely in V_0. It follows that the image of m and so that of i is zero, as was to be shown.

What has just been proved is rather weaker than the statement of the present lemma, namely that the image of the injection $H_q(V(\lambda), V_0) \to H_q(V(K), V_0)$ is zero for $q \leq r - 1$, under the induction hypothesis. This stronger result will now be derived. Let K' be a disc on S smaller than K, contained in it, and still containing the special points $z_1, z_2, \ldots, z_h$ in its interior. Let M be the closure of $S - K'$. Consider the following diagram:

$$H_q(V(K), V(K \cap M)) \xrightarrow{\ j\ } H_q(V, V(M))$$

$$\uparrow k \qquad\qquad\qquad \uparrow$$

$$H_q(V(\lambda), V_0) \xrightarrow{\ i_1\ } H_q(V(K), V_0) \xrightarrow{\ i_2\ } H(V, V_0)$$

$$\uparrow l$$

$$H_q(V(K \cap M), V_0)$$

All the homomorphisms appearing are those induced by the appropriate inclusions. It has already been shown that the image of $i_2 i_1$ is zero. From the commutativity of the square in the diagram it follows that the image of $j k i_1$ is zero. But, by Theorem 7, j is an isomorphism for all q, and so the image of $k i_1$ is zero. That is to say, the image of i_1 is in the kernel of k, which is the image of l, since the vertical line is part of an exact homology sequence, namely that of the triple $(V(K), V(K \cap M), V_0)$.

The proof will now be completed by showing that

$$H_q(V(K \cap M), V_0)$$

is zero for all $q \leq r - 1$. An application of the corollary to Theorem 10 gives

$$H_q(V(K \cap M), V_0) \cong H_q(X(K \cap M), X'(K \cap M) \cup V_0)$$

Here one is dealing with a fibre bundle over an annulus as base, and it is not hard to see, either by breaking $K \cap M$ into cells or by a spectral sequence argument, that

$$H_q(X(K \cap M), X'(K \cap M) \cup V_0)$$
$$\cong H_1(K \cap M, z_0; H_{q-1}(V_0, P)),$$

where the semicolon denotes homology with the local coefficients $H_{q-1}(V_0, P)$. This last group is zero, by the induction hypothesis, for $q \leq r - 1$, and so the required result follows.

Although the homology groups are here assumed to have integer coefficients, it is clear that all results up to this point would hold for an arbitrary coefficient group.

2. Statement of Lefschetz's second main theorem

In the following statement of this theorem λ, C', z_0, and V_0 have the meanings already introduced.

THEOREM 19. **(1)** $H_r(V(\lambda), V_0)$ *is infinite cyclic, with a generator to be denoted by* $\bar{\Delta}^{(r)}$.

(2) *There is a continuous mapping* f: $(E^r, S^{r-1}) \to (V(\lambda), V_0)$ *where* E^r *is a solid* r-*sphere and* S^{r-1} *its boundary, such that* $\bar{\Delta}^{(r)}$ *is the image under the induced homomorphism* f_*: $H_r(E^r, S^{r-1}) \to H_r(V(\lambda), V_0)$ *of a generator* $\bar{\Delta}_0^{(r)}$ *of* $H_r(E^r, S^{r-1})$. *Also* z_0 *can be chosen so that the image of* f *is contained in a preassigned neighbourhood of* C'.

(3) *Let* U *be a preassigned neighbourhood of* C'. *Then there is a neighbourhood* U' *of* C' *such that, if* $f(E^r) \subset U'$ *and if* f' *is a second mapping of* (E^r, S^{r-1}) *into* $(V(\lambda) \cap U', V_0 \cap U')$ *satisfying* (2), *then* f *and* f', *regarded as mappings into* $(V(\lambda) \cap U, V_0 \cap U)$ *are homotopic.*

As in the case of Theorem 18 this will be proved by induction on r, the result being clearly true for curves in relation to a sufficiently general hyperplane pencil; and until further notice the term "induction hypothesis" will mean the assumption of the above theorem for dimension less than r.

3. Sketch proof of Theorem 19

The proof of Theorem 19 is rather complicated, and so the details will be left over to the next chapter, the present section being intended merely to give a geometrical picture of the proof. The notation is to be as introduced in §2 of Chapter III. In particular, w is to be taken as the parameter of a second pencil Π' the hyperplane of which through C' cuts V in a non-singular section; this is possible by Theorem 13 (e). Let the hyperplane of Π' through C' have parameter w'. Then the point C' projects from the linear space L into the point (z', w') of the (z, w)-plane L_0. Part (c) of Theorem 13 ensures that (z', w') is a simple point of the curve Γ. Thus in the (z, w)-plane there is a neighbourhood N of (z', w') which is an open 4-cell and is such that $N \cap \Gamma$ is a 2-cell. It may be assumed that N is specified by inequalities of the type $|z - z'| < k, |w - w'| < k$. $V'(w)$ will denote the section of V by the hyperplane of parameter w in the pencil Π'.

If z is sufficiently close to z', part (d) of Theorem 13 implies that there are two values of w, say $w_1(z)$, $w_2(z)$, such that $V(z, w_1(z))$ and $V(z, w_2(z))$ have singularities $C_1(z)$, $C_2(z)$ in a preassigned neighbourhood of C'. On the other hand, part (c) of Theorem 13 implies that the line $z = z'$ in the (z, w)-plane is the tangent to Γ at the point (z', w'), and so, if w is sufficiently close to w', there will be exactly one point $(z(w), w)$ on Γ such that $z(w)$ is an analytic function of w, tending to z' as w tends to w'.

As z traces out the arc λ, the points $w_1(z)$, $w_2(z)$ in the complex w-plane trace out two arcs which will be called λ_1 and λ_2. It is not hard to verify that $w_1(z)$, $w_2(z)$, are roots of a quadratic equation whose coefficients are analytic in z, and in fact can be written as $a(z) \pm b(z)\sqrt{z - z'}$, where $a(z)$ and $b(z)$ are analytic in z around z'. If t is the parameter on λ (equal to 0 at z') set $t = s^2$. It is then clear that the union of λ_1 and λ_2 can be parametrized analytically in terms of s. This union will be called λ'. λ' is thus an analytic image of the interval $-\sqrt{\rho} \leq s \leq \sqrt{\rho}$, where λ is bounded by $0 \leq t \leq \rho$.

The construction of the element $\bar{\Delta}^{(r)}$ of Theorem 19, and the corresponding vanishing cycles, in Lefschetz's terminology, will now be described in diagrammatic fashion.

STEP I. In Fig. 1 the rectangle (drawn in perspective) on

the right is to represent $V(z_1)$ for a suitable z_1 on λ and the vertical lines represent sections of V by $(n - 2)$-spaces through L, as marked in the diagram. The curved arc with C' marked on it represents a portion of the curve C. The two hemispheres embedded in $V(z_1)$ and marked $\Delta_1^{(r-1)}$ and $\Delta_2^{(r-1)}$ are relative $(r - 1)$-cycles of $V(z_1, \lambda_i')$ modulo $V(z_1, w_i)$ for $i = 1, 2$, respectively, where w_1 and w_2 are points on λ' near $w_1(z_1)$, $w_2(z_1)$

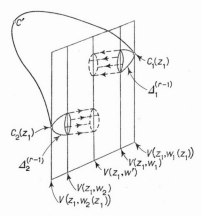

Fig. 1

respectively and λ_i' is the portion of λ' joining w_i to $w_i(z_1)$, for $i = 1, 2$. $\Delta_1^{(r-1)}$ and $\Delta_2^{(r-1)}$ are to be as described in the induction hypothesis, applied to $V(z_1)$, and are to be constructed in neighbourhoods of $C_1(z_1)$, $C_2(z_1)$, respectively. The first step here is to construct a homotopy which will pull the bases of the hemispheres $\Delta_1^{(r-1)}$ and $\Delta_2^{(r-1)}$ back into $V(z_1, w')$.

This operation is marked in the diagram by the broken lines with the arrows. The new positions of the bases of these hemispheres will be called $\delta_1^{(r-2)}$, $\delta_2^{(r-2)}$ respectively. Eventually it will be shown that $\delta_1^{(r-2)}$ and $\delta_2^{(r-2)}$ can be joined up by a cylinder so that the stretched $\Delta_1^{(r-1)}$, $\Delta_2^{(r-1)}$ along with this cylinder form a sphere which will be the vanishing cycle attached to C', and the base of the relative cycle $\Delta^{(r)}$ whose existence is to be proved.

STEP II. In Fig. 2 the "stretched" relative cycle $\Delta_1^{(r-1)}$ is still called $\Delta_1^{(r-1)}$. It is now a relative cycle of $V(z_1, \lambda_1)$ modulo

$V(z_1, w')$. The application of the induction hypothesis to $V(\lambda, w')$ shows the existence of a relative $(r - 1)$ -cycle $\Delta_3^{(r-1)}$ of $V(\lambda, w')$ modulo $V(z_1, w')$. Now it can be assumed (as will be shown later) that all the operations being described can be carried out in a preassigned neighbourhood of C', whose intersection with $V'(w')$ can thus be assumed to be homologically

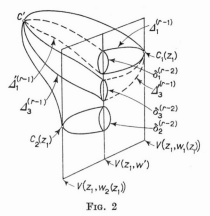

FIG. 2

trivial. Thus $\delta_1^{(r-2)}$ is the boundary of a chain $\Delta_1'^{(r-1)}$ on $V'(w')$, and in fact a slight adjustment ensures that $\Delta_1'^{(r-1)}$ is in $V(\lambda, w')$. Applying the induction hypothesis, it follows that $\Delta_1'^{(r-1)}$ is homologous modulo $V(z_1, w')$ to $k\Delta_3^{(r-1)}$ for some integer k. Thus $\delta_1^{(r-2)} \sim k\delta_3^{(r-2)}$ for some integer k where $\delta_3^{(r-2)} = d\Delta_3^{(r-1)}$. It must be shown now that $k = \pm 1$. To do this a homotopy similar to that used in Step I to stretch the $\Delta_i^{(r-1)}$ is applied to shrink $\delta_3^{(r-2)}$ in $V(z_1, \lambda_1)$ down to the point $C_1(z_1)$. Thus $\delta_3^{(r-2)}$ is the boundary of a chain $\Delta_3'^{(r-1)}$ in $V(z_1, \lambda_1)$. The induction hypothesis, applied in $V(z_1, \lambda_1)$ shows then that $\Delta_3'^{(r-1)}$ is homologous modulo $V(z_1, w')$ to $k'\Delta_1^{(r-1)}$ for some integer k'. Taking boundaries, it follows that $\delta_3^{(r-2)} \sim k'\delta_3^{(r)-2}$. Thus $(kk' - 1)\delta_3^{(r-2)} \sim 0$ in $V(z_1, w')$. When this is done in detail it will turn out that all these operations can still be made to work in a preassigned neighbourhood of C', and a lemma will later be proved to show that, in a small enough neighbourhood of C', $\delta_3^{(r-2)}$ is not rationally homologous to zero on $V(z_1, w)$. Thus the homology $(kk' - 1)\delta_3^{(r-2)} \sim 0$ implies

$k = \pm 1$. Part (3) of the induction hypothesis, applied in $V'(w')$ to the two mappings of a hemisphere into $V'(w')$ giving rise to $\Delta_3^{(r-1)}$ and $\Delta_1'^{(r-1)}$ shows that $\delta_1^{(r-2)}$ and $\delta_3^{(r-2)}$ can be joined up in $V(z_1, w')$ by a cylinder (product of an interval and a $(r-2)$-sphere); and similarly $\delta_2^{(r-2)}$ and $\delta_3^{(r-2)}$. Thus $\Delta_1^{(r-1)}$, $\Delta_2^{(r-1)}$ and the cylinder joining their bases form a spherical cycle $\delta^{(r-1)}$ in a neighbourhood of C'. This neighbourhood can be preassigned as a geodesic sphere, and so $\delta^{(r-1)}$ can be taken as the base of an r-hemisphere $\Delta^{(r)}$ embedded in V. A further adjustment will enable $\Delta^{(r)}$ to be compressed into $V(\lambda)$. This completes the description of the construction of $\Delta^{(r)}$. The second stage in the proof of Theorem 19 will consist in showing that $\Delta^{(r)}$ represents a homology class $\bar{\Delta}^{(r)}$ of $V(\lambda)$ modulo $V(z_0)$ which satisfies the conditions of that theorem. This will now be carried out in Step III.

STEP III. The outline to be given here, as in the previous two steps, entirely glosses over the difficulties caused by having to ensure that all operations are carried out in a preassigned neighbourhood of C'. Some other refinements are also left unmentioned until the actual details of the proof are considered below.

It has to be shown first that a relative r-cycle γ of $V(\lambda)$ modulo $V(z_1)$ is homologous to a multiple of $\Delta^{(r)}$ in V modulo $V(z_1)$. By Theorem 16, γ may be assumed to be a singular chain on a preassigned neighbourhood of C'. Let μ be the boundary of γ. In Fig. 3, the oval shape in the middle represents $\delta^{(r-1)}$, the irregular outline represents μ and the rectangle is $V(z_1)$. μ may first be adjusted to lie in $V(z_1, \lambda')$. An application of the induction hypothesis in $V(z_1, \lambda_1)$ and $V(z_1, \lambda_2)$ then shows that μ is homologous to a cycle represented diagrammatically by the irregular outline in Fig. 4. That is μ is homologous to a chain consisting of multiples of the parts of $\delta^{(r-1)}$ near $C_1(z_1)$ and $C_2(z_2)$ (it will turn out in fact that these multiples have the same coefficient c, say) and a chain which does not meet the singular sections $V(z_1, w_1(z_1))$ and $V(z_1, w_2(z_1))$. The homotopy already employed in Step I compresses this last mentioned chain into $V(z_1, w')$. Thus

$\mu - c\delta^{(r-1)}$ is homologous to a cycle in $V(z_1, w')$ represented in Fig. 5 by the two small loops at the top and bottom. Applying again the homotopy of Step I (or rather the situation is more similar to the shrinkage of $\delta_3^{(r-2)}$ to a point in Step II) it turns out that $\mu - c\delta^{(r-1)}$ is homologous to zero in $V(z_1, \lambda')$.

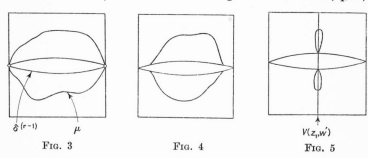

$\delta^{(r-1)}$ μ

FIG. 3   FIG. 4   FIG. 5

$V(z_1, w')$

Since $\mu = d\gamma$ and $\delta^{(r-1)} = d\Delta^{(r)}$ it follows that $\gamma - c\Delta^{(r)}$ added to some chain on $V(z_1)$ is a cycle on V, and, as will be seen later, on an arbitrarily small neighbourhood of C', which may be assumed to be homologically trivial. It follows at once that γ is homologous to $c\Delta^{(r)}$ in V modulo $V(z_1)$, as required.

STEP IV. Having carried out Steps I, II, III it remains to be shown that the various parts of Theorem 19 are satisfied. In this verification the only hard part is part (3), the proof of which is in effect a copy of the Hurewicz isomorphism theorem, modifications being necessary only to ensure that everything is carried out in a preassigned neighbourhood of C'.

It is desirable at this stage to insert a note on the proof of Theorem 19 in the case where there are no special points on S. The statement of the theorem reduces in this case to $H_r(V, V_0) = 0$. This follows at once from the corollary to Theorem 10. For $H_r(V, V_0) \cong H_r(X(S), X'(S) \cup V_0)$, in the notation of Theorem 10, and this is isomorphic to $H_{r-2}(V_0, P) \otimes H_2(S, z_0)$, which is zero by Theorem 17.

4. Some immediate consequences

The following theorem is obtained by combining Theorems 15 and 19. The fact that $H_{r-2}(V_0, P) = 0$ (required for the application of Theorem 15) is now known by Theorem 17.

THEOREM 20. z_0 and the z_i and the paths λ_i being as in §3, Chapter III, there is a "hemispherical" relative cycle Δ_i on $V(\lambda_i)$ modulo V_0 such that $H_r(V, V_0)$ is generated by the relative homology classes of the Δ_i. Moreover, if z_0 is taken sufficiently close to z_i, Δ_i may be assumed to be a singular chain on a preassigned neighbourhood of C_i, the singularity on $V(z_i)$. (Lefschetz [9], p. 93, Theorem VI.)

Taking the boundaries of the Δ_i and applying the exactness of the homology sequences of the pair (V, V_0) and of the triple (V, V_0, P) the following is obtained:

THEOREM 21. The boundary of Δ_i is a "spherical" cycle δ_i on V_0 and the kernels of the two injection maps $H_{r-1}(V_0) \to H_{r-1}(V)$ and $H_{r-1}(V_0, P) \to H_{r-1}(V, P)$ are both generated by the homology classes, in the appropriate sense, of the δ_i. And if z_0 is taken sufficiently near to z_i, δ_i may be taken as a chain on a preassigned neighbourhood of C_i. (Lefschetz [9], p. 93, Theorem V.)

In addition if Δ_i and δ_i are constructed in a sufficiently small neighbourhood of C_i, they are defined up to a homotopy, in the sense described more precisely in Theorem 19, part (3).

Let V_r, V_{r-1}, V_{r-2}, ... be a sequence of non-singular algebraic varieties such that V_i is a hyperplane section of V_{i+1} for each i. Then a simple inductive argument, starting from Theorem 17 and making use of the exactness of the homology sequence of a triple, establishes the following results:

THEOREM 22. $H_q(V_r, V_s) = 0$ for $q \leqslant s$, and consequently the injection map $H_q(V_s, V_t) \to H_q(V_r, V_t)$ is an isomorphism onto for $q \leq s - 1$, and is onto for $q = s$. Moreover the kernel of the injection $H_s(V_s, V_t) \to H_s(V_r, V_t)$ is the same as that of the injection $H_s(V_s, V_t) \to H_s(V_{s+1}, V_t)$ and is the image of the boundary homomorphism $H_{s+1}(V_{s+1}, V_s) \to H_s(V_s, V_t)$.

Note that in the last remark $H_{s+1}(V_{s+1}, V_s)$ is a group of the type described by Theorem 19 and so the kernel of the $H_s(V_s, V_t) \to H_s(V_{s+1}, V_t)$ is expressed in terms of something which is not altogether unfamiliar.

CHAPTER V

PROOF OF LEFSCHETZ'S SECOND THEOREM

1. Deformation theorems

It is clear that the method sketched in the last chapter for the proof of Theorem 19 depends on some mechanism which will provide the necessary deformations and shrinkings, a mechanism which, in addition, allows these operations to be carried out in an arbitrary neighbourhood of C', in the notation already introduced in §3, Chapter III. In this section two theorems will be proved which will enable the details of the proof sketched in §3, Chapter IV to be carried out.

The two arcs λ_1 and λ_2 in the complex w-plane have already been introduced in §3, Chapter IV; they are the arcs traced out by the two values of $w(z)$ as z traces the arc λ in the z-plane. Also if t is the parameter on λ then $\lambda_1 \cup \lambda_2 = \lambda'$ can be parametrized by s where $s^2 = t$. For the point z on λ with parameter t the two corresponding values of $w(z)$, namely $w_1(z)$ and $w_2(z)$, have parameter values $+\sqrt{t}$ and $-\sqrt{t}$ on λ'.

Consider now the following set $\sum$, a subset of $\lambda \times \lambda'$, which in its turn is a subset, namely a 2-cell, of the (z, w)-plane. $\sum$ is to consist of the points (z, w) where $z \in \lambda$, of parameter t, say, and $w \in \lambda'$ of parameter s such that $-\sqrt{t} \leqslant s \leqslant +\sqrt{t}$. It is not hard to see that $\sum$ is a 2-cell which can be assumed, by taking λ small enough, to be contained in a neighbourhood of (z', w'), a neighbourhood which can be assumed to be a 4-cell, and that the boundary of $\sum$ is formed by the set of all points $(z, w(z))$ on Γ for $z \in \lambda$, along with points (z_0, w) for $w \in \lambda'$.

Now since $\sum$ is a 2-cell embedded differentiably (apart from two corners on its boundary at $(z_0, w_1(z_0))$ and $(z_0, w_1(z_0))$) in the (z, w)-plane, it is not hard to see that a neighbourhood of

Σ can be taken as K and $\sum$ itself as E in the notation of §1, Chapter II, and a shrinking family F of curves can be constructed satisfying the conditions stated in that section. It follows from Theorem 12 that, if N is a suitable neighbourhood of $\sum$ in the (z, w)-plane, then $\bigcup\limits_{(z,w)\in\Sigma} V(z, w)$ is a deformation re-tract of $\bigcup\limits_{(z,w)\in N} V(z, w)$.

Now let U be a preassigned neighbourhood of C'. In the retraction just mentioned C' is fixed, and so, throughout the deformation all points of a sufficiently small neighbourhood U_1 of C' remain within U. Suppose U_1 projects from L onto a set U_0 in the (z, w)-plane, and, by taking z_0 sufficiently near to z', arrange that $\sum \subset U_1$ (if z_0 is moved nearer to z' on λ this simply means slicing a piece off $\sum$ as already constructed). Also, the neighbourhood N mentioned above can be assumed to be contained in U_1 and to consist of points (z, w) with $z \in N_1$, $w \in N_2$, where N_1 and N_2 are neighbourhoods of z' and w' respectively in the complex z- and w-planes. Having made these arrangements, the following theorem sums up the results obtained:

THEOREM 23. *Let U be a given neighbourhood of C' in V. Then if U_1, N_1, N_2 are sufficiently small neighbourhoods of C' in V, z' in the z-plane, and w' in the w-plane, respectively, and z_0 is so chosen that $\sum \subset N_1 \times N_2$, there is a homotopy of the inclusion mapping $V(N_1, N_2) \cap U_1 \to U$ into a mapping whose image is contained in $\bigcup V(z, w)$, the union being taken over all $(z, w) \in \sum$.*

The second deformation theorem to be proved here is concerned with deformations carried out within a set of the type $V(z, \lambda'')$, where z is some point on λ and λ'' is an arc on λ' contained strictly between $w_1(z)$ and $w_2(z)$. The $V(z, w)$ contained in such a set $V(z, \lambda'')$ are all non-singular, and so of course Theorem 5 could be applied. The refinement needed here is something to ensure that deformations can be carried out in a given neighbourhood of C'.

The required theorem will be obtained with the aid of a family F' of curves constructed as in §1, Chapter II. The set

K of that section is to be replaced by $\sum$, and E by $\sum \cap \Gamma$. The curves F are to be those joining (z_0, w) to $(z(w), w)$, for each $w \in \lambda'$, obtained by letting z vary along λ from z_0 to $z(w)$. If $t(w)$ is the parameter on λ of $z(w)$, for $w \in \lambda'$, then the parameter on the member of F corresponding to $w \in \lambda'$ is to be $t - t(w)$. This ensures that a parameter is chosen for the curves of F' in such a way that the points on $V(z(w), w)$, $w \in \lambda'$, all have parameter 0.

Next let λ_0' be the sub-arc of λ' obtained by removing the points $w_1(z_0)$ and $w_2(z_0)$. The points (z_0, w) with $w \in \lambda_0'$ are all ordinary and so, removing the points of the linear space L from $V(z_0, \lambda_0')$, a fibre bundle is obtained which is clearly trivial. That is to say, $V(z_0, \lambda_0') - L$ is homeomorphic to $(V(z_0, w') - L) \times \lambda_0'$. Any point of $V(z_0, \lambda_0') - L$ can thus be written as (p, s), where $p \in V(z_0, w')$ and s is the parameter of a point on λ'.

The first step in obtaining the required deformation theorem is to prove the following lemma:

LEMMA. *Let U be a given neighbourhood of C' in V. Then there are a neighbourhood U' of C' and numbers δ and η such that, if a curve of F' passing through $(p, s) \in V(z_0, \lambda_0') - L$ meets U', all points of parameter less than δ on the curve of F' through (p, s'), for any s' such that $|s - s'| < \eta$, lie in U.*

PROOF. Let $\bar{U}_1$ be a closed neighbourhood of C'. By Lemma e, §2, Chapter II, the mapping $f : V(z_0, \lambda_0') \to V$, which assigns to each point $q \in V(z_0, \lambda_0')$ the point of parameter zero on the curve of F' through q, is continuous. And so $f(\bar{U}_1)$ is a closed compact set G on $V(z_0, \lambda')$. If U_1 is small enough it is clear that $G \subset V(z_0, \lambda_0') - L$. Then, as noted above, any point $q \in G$ can be written as a pair (p, s) with $p \in V(z_0, w')$ and $s \in \lambda_0'$. Assume $\bar{U}_1 \subset U$, so that, for $q \in G$, $f(q)$ will lie in U. Then, by the lemmas of §2, Chapter II, there is a neighbourhood $U(q)$ of q in $V(z_0, \lambda_0') - L$ and a number $\delta(q)$ such that all points of parameter less than $\delta(q)$ on curves of F' through $U(q)$ are contained in U. Now $U(q)$ can be specified as consisting of points (p', s') such that p' is in a neighbourhood of p on $V(z_0, w')$ and $|s - s'| < \eta(q)$ for some positive number $\eta(q)$. In particular it follows that all points of parameter less than $\delta(q)$ on curves of F' through points (p, s') for $|s - s'| < \eta(q)$ are in U. But G is compact and so can be covered by a finite number of the $U(q)$. Let δ and η be the minima of the corresponding finite collections of $\delta(q)$ and $\eta(q)$. And, finally, use Lemma e, §2, Chapter II to find a neighbourhood U' such that any curve of F meeting it ends in U_1. Then U', δ, η have the asserted properties.

Using the notations of this lemma, choose a point z_1 on λ such that the parameters on curves of F' of all points of the $V(z_1, w)$ with w on λ' between $w_1(z_1)$ and $w_2(z_1)$ are $< \delta$, and also so that the difference in parameters of $w_1(z_1)$ and $w_2(z_1)$ on λ' is less than η. Let λ'' denote any arc on λ' between but not including $w_1(z_1)$ and $w_2(z_1)$. Then the following is the deformation theorem required for the working of this chapter:

THEOREM 24. *Let U be a preassigned neighbourhood of C'. Then there are a neighbourhood U' of C' and a point z_1 on λ with the following properties: if ϕ: $X \to U \cap V(z_1, \lambda'')$ is a continuous mapping whose image is in U', and $\psi(p)$, for $p \in X$, is the point on λ'' such that $\phi(p) \in V(z_1, \psi(p))$, and if θ is a mapping of λ'' into itself homotopic to the identity, then there is a mapping $\phi' : X \to U \cap V(z_1, \lambda'')$ homotopic to ϕ (that is to say, homotopic as mappings into $U \cap V(z_1, \lambda'')$) such that $\phi'(p) \in V(z_1, \theta_0\psi(p))$.*

PROOF. U' is to be as in the above lemma, z_1 and λ'' as described just before the statement of this theorem. Now introduce the following mappings. Given $q \in V(z_1, \lambda'')$ there is a unique curve of F' through it intersecting $V(z_0, \lambda'') - L \subset V(z_0, \lambda_0') - L$ in a point (p, s). Define the mapping g by $g(q) = (p, s)$. Next, for a point $(p, s) \in V(z_0, \lambda'') - L$, define $h(p, s) = (p, \theta(s))$. Finally, noting that g is a homeomorphism, its inverse $\overset{-1}{g}$ is defined, and so the mapping $\phi' : X \to U \cap V(z_1, \lambda'')$ can be defined as $\phi'(q) = \overset{-1}{g_0}h_0g_0\phi(q)$ for $q \in X$. To check that ϕ' has the required properties, suppose that $\Theta : \lambda' \times I \to \lambda''$ is a mapping such that $\Theta(w, 0) = w$ and

$\Theta(w, 1) = \theta(w)$. Define Φ on $X \times I$ by setting $\Phi(q, t) = \overset{-1}{g_o} H(g_o \phi(q), t)$, where $H(p, s, t) = (p, \Theta(s, t))$. Φ clearly defines a homotopy of ϕ and ϕ', and the above lemma ensures that its image is in $U \cap V(z_1, \lambda'')$ as required. Also the construction of ϕ' ensures that $\phi'(p) \in V(z_1, \theta_o \psi(p))$.

There are many variations and generalizations of this theorem. One variation in particular which will be needed in the subsequent working is the following:

COROLLARY. *Let U, U', z_1, λ'' and ϕ be as in the above theorem. Then there is a mapping $\phi' : X \to V(z_1, w_1(z_1)) \cap U$ such that ϕ and ϕ' are homotopic as mappings into $V(z_1, \lambda') \cap U$.*

PROOF. The proof is as for the main theorem, the homotopy Θ being replaced by the operation of shrinking λ'' onto the point $w_1(z_1)$ on λ'. It should be noted that $\overset{-1}{g}$ is still defined in this situation for points on $V(z_0, w_1(z_1))$.

Clearly a similar result would hold for $w_2(z_1)$.

2. Some remarks on Theorem 19

Preliminary to giving the details of the proof of Theorem 19, one or two results will be obtained, to be used not only in proving this theorem, but also serving to strengthen it.

THEOREM 25. *Let U be a preassigned neighbourhood of C'. Then the point z_0 on the arc λ ending at z' may be chosen, and a neighbourhood U' of C' may be found such that there is a mapping $j: (U', U' \cap V(z_0)) \to (U, U \cap V(z_0))$ homotopic to the inclusion mapping and such that $j(U') \subset V(\lambda)$.*

PROOF. For if N is a small circular neighbourhood of z' on S, a family of curves in N may be constructed with the properties described in §1, Chapter II, K and E being replaced by N and λ, respectively. Then by Theorem 12 there is a deformation retraction of $V(N)$ on $V(\lambda)$, C' being fixed throughout the deformation. It follows at once that a sufficiently small neighbourhood U' of C' will remain in U throughout the deformation. It only remains to choose z_0 so that $V(z_0)$ meets U'.

THEOREM 26. *Let U be a given neighbourhood of C'. Then there is a neighbourhood U' of C' such that any cycle μ on*

$V(z_0) \cap U'$, z_0 being suitably chosen, is homologous to zero in $V(\lambda) \cap U$.

PROOF. For U' may always be chosen to be homologically trivial and also so that U, U', z_0 satisfy the conditions of Theorem 25.

THEOREM 27. Let $\Delta^{(r)}$ be the relative cycle whose existence is asserted by Theorem 19, and write $d\Delta^{(r)} = \delta^{(r-1)}$. If U is any neighbourhood of C', Theorem 19 implies that $\delta^{(r-1)}$ can be constructed as a cycle on $U \cap V_0$. Then U can be chosen so that $c\delta^{(r-1)}$ is not homologous to zero in $U \cap V_0$ for any integer c.

PROOF. For choose U to be, in the first place, homologically trivial, and suppose that $c\delta^{(r-1)} = d\theta$, where θ is a singular chain on $U \cap V_0$. Then $c\Delta^{(r)} - \theta$ is a cycle on U and so is homologous to zero in U. That is to say, $c\Delta^{(r)}$ is homologous to zero modulo $U \cap V_0$ in the relative homology of U modulo $U \cap V_0$, or, more simply, homologous to zero modulo V_0 in the relative homology of $V(N)$ modulo V_0, where N is a neighbourhood of z' such that $V(N) \supset U$. But U and N can be chosen (Theorem 25) so that the pair $(V(\lambda), V_0)$ is a deformation retract of the pair $(V(N), V_0)$ and so the fact that $\bar{\Delta}^{(r)}$ is a generator of the infinite cyclic group $H_r(V(\lambda), V_0)$ would be contradicted.

THEOREM 28. (1) Suppose that $f : (E^r, S^{r-1}) \to (V(\lambda), V_0)$ has been constructed and $f_* \bar{\Delta}_0^{(r)} = \bar{\Delta}^{(r)}$. To prove parts (1) and (2) of Theorem 19 it is sufficient to show that, if U is a given neighbourhood of C', there is a neighbourhood U' of C' such that, if the image of f is in U' and if γ is a relative r-cycle of $V(\lambda) \cap U'$ modulo $V_0 \cap U'$, then γ is homologous to a multiple of $\Delta^{(r)}$ in U modulo $U \cap V_0$, and that no multiple of $\Delta^{(r)}$ is homologous to zero in $V(\lambda)$ modulo V_0.

(2) If f and f' are as in the statement of Theorem 19, in order to prove part (3) of that theorem it is sufficient to show that, given any neighbourhood U of C', there is a neighbourhood U' of C' such that, if the images of f and f' are in U' then f and f' are homotopic as mappings into the pair $(U, U \cap V_0)$.

PROOF. (1) follows from Theorems 16 and 25, and (2) follows from Theorem 25.

3. Formal verification of Theorem 19; the vanishing cycle

In this section Steps I and II (§3, Chapter IV) will be checked in detail. Let z_1 be a point on λ and let λ'' be the subarc of λ' joining $w_1(z_1)$, $w_2(z_1)$ (cf. Chapter IV for notation). If M_1, M_2 are respectively given neighbourhoods of $C_1(z_1)$ and $C_2(z_1)$ then there are maps

$$f_i : (E^{r-1}, S^{r-2}) \to (V(z_1, \lambda'') \cap M_i, V(z_1, w_i) \cap M_i)$$

for $i = 1$, 2, where w_1, w_2 are on λ'' and sufficiently near its ends (Induction Hypothesis (2)).

If U_0 is a given neighbourhood of C', and z_1, M_1, M_2 are suitably chosen, there are maps

$$f'_i : (E^{r-1}, S^{r-2}) \to (V(z_1, \lambda'') \cap U_0, V(z_1, w_1) \cap U_0), \quad i = 1, 2.$$

(Application of Theorem 24 to f_1, f_2 with the homotopy on λ'' being that which shrinks the arc $w_1 w_2$ to the point w').

Let $\bar{\Delta}_0^{(r-1)}$ be a generator of $H_{r-1}(E^{r-1}, S^{r-2})$, $\Delta_0^{(r-1)}$ a representative relative cycle. Write $\bar{\Delta}_i^{(r-1)} = f'_{i*} \bar{\Delta}_0^{(r-1)}$ for $i = 1$, 2 and let $\Delta_i^{(r-1)}$ be the representative of $\bar{\Delta}_i^{(r-1)}$ obtained by applying f'_i to $\Delta_0^{(r-1)}$. Write $\delta_i^{(r-2)} = d\Delta_i^{(r-1)}$ for $i = 1$, 2.

There is a map

$$f_3 : (E^{r-1}, S^{r-2}) \to (V(\lambda, w') \cap U_0, V(z_1, w') \cap U_0),$$

(Induction Hypothesis, part (2)), carrying $\Delta_0^{(r-1)}$ into $\Delta_3^{(r-1)}$, say. Write $d\Delta_3^{(r-1)} = \delta_3^{(r-2)}$.

The next part of the verification applies to Step II, the setting up of homotopies between f'_1, f'_2, f_3.

If U_1 is a given neighbourhood of C', U_0 can be chosen so that $\delta_1^{(r-2)}$ is homologous to zero in $V(\lambda, w') \cap U_1$. (Theorem 26). Write $\delta_1^{(r-2)} = d\Delta_1'^{(r-1)}$, where $\Delta_1'^{(r-1)}$ is a singular chain on $V(\lambda, w') \cap U_1$.

U_2 being a given neighbourhood of C', U_1 can be chosen so that $\Delta_1'^{(r-1)} \sim k\Delta_3^{(r-1)}$ in the relative homology of $V(\lambda, w') \cap U_2$ modulo $V(z_1, w') \cap U_2$ (Induction Hypothesis). k is an integer, to be proved $= \pm 1$.

$\delta_3^{(r-2)}$ is a cycle on $V(z_1, w') \cap U_2$. If U_3 is a given neighbourhood of C', U_2 may be chosen so that $\delta_3^{(r-2)}$ is homologous in $V(z_1, \lambda') \cap U_3$ to a cycle δ on $V(z_1, w_1(z_1)) \cap U_3$. (By the corollary to Theorem 24, the homotopy on λ'' being one which moves w' to $w_1(z_1)$.) It may be assumed, by choosing U_3 suitably, that $V'(w) \cap U_3$ is empty or homologically trivial for each $w \in \lambda'$, and so δ is homologous to zero in $V'(w_1(z_1)) \cap U_3$. U_4 being a given neighbourhood of C', U_3 may be chosen so that δ is homologous to zero in $V(z_1, w_1(z_1)) \cap U_4$ (Theorem 12).

Thus $\delta_3^{(r-2)}$ is homologous to zero in $V(z_1, \lambda') \cap U_4$ (assuming $U_{i+1} \supset U_i$ for each i). Write $\delta_3^{(r-2)} = d\Delta_3'^{(r-1)}$, where $\Delta_3'^{(r-1)}$ is a singular chain on $V(z_1, \lambda') \cap U_4$. By the argument which is given in detail below, at the beginning of the verification of Step III, U_4 can be chosen so that $\Delta_3'^{(r-1)} \sim k'\Delta_1^{(r-1)}$ in the relative homology of $V(z_1, \lambda') \cap U_5$ modulo $V(z_1, w') \cap U_5$, where k' is an integer and U_5 is a given neighbourhood of C'.

Taking boundaries in the homologies $\Delta_1'^{(r-1)} \sim k\Delta_3^{(r-1)}$ and $\Delta_3'^{(r-1)} \sim k'\Delta_1^{(r-1)}$ and still assuming $U_i \subset U_{i+1}$ for each i, it follows that $\delta_1'^{(r-2)} \sim k\delta_3^{(r-2)}$ and $\delta_3^{(r-2)} \sim k'\delta_1^{(r-2)}$ both homologies in $V(z_1, w') \cap U_5$. Thus $(1 - kk')\delta_3^{(r-2)} \sim 0$ in $V(z_1, w') \cap U_5$. By Theorem 27, U_5 can be chosen so that this implies $kk' - 1 = 0$, i.e. $k = \pm 1$.

And now the Induction Hypothesis, part (3), applied in $V(\lambda, w')$, implies that, if U is a given neighbourhood of C', U_5 can be chosen so that f_1' and f_3, restricted to S^{r-2}, are homotopic as maps into $V(z_1, w') \cap U$.

Thus, given the neighbourhood U of C', there is a neighbourhood U_0 of C' such that, if f_1' and f_3 are constructed to have images in U_0, then, restricted to S^{r-2}, they are homotopic as maps into $V(z_1, w') \cap U$. A similar statement may be made concerning f_2'. It is thus clear that a map $f : S^{r-1} \to V(z_1, \lambda') \cap U$ may be constructed such that, if $\Delta_1^{(r-1)}$, $\Delta_2^{(r-1)}$ have the right signs, there is a singular chain ν satisfying $\delta^{(r-1)} = \Delta_1^{(r-1)} + \Delta_2^{(r-1)} + \nu$, where $\delta^{(r-1)}$ is a representative of the image under f of a generator of $H_{r-1}(S^{r-1})$.

$\delta^{(r-1)}$ is the required vanishing cycle, constructed in a preassigned neighbourhood U of C'. In addition, U being preassigned, say as an open cell, Theorem 25 shows that a neighbourhood U' of C' may be chosen, such that, if $\delta^{(r-1)}$ is constructed in U', then f can be extended to a map of (E^r, S^{r-1}) into $(V(\lambda) \cap U, V(z_1) \cap U)$. If $\Delta^{(r)}$ represents the image under f_* of a generator of $H_r(E^r, S^{r-1})$, then $\delta^{(r-1)} = d\Delta^{(r)}$. $\Delta^{(r)}$ will be shown to satisfy the conditions of Theorem 19.

4. Proof of Theorem 19, parts (1) and (2)

In this section Step III will be checked, and along with it, the proof of the homology $\Delta_3'^{(r-1)} \sim k'\Delta_1^{(r-1)}$ which was left incomplete in §3.

Let γ be a relative r-cycle of $V(\lambda)$ modulo $V(z_1)$, ($V(z_1)$ is being used here in place of $V(z_0)$) and assume, as already mentioned in the summary of Step III, that γ is a singular chain on a neighbourhood U_1 of C'.

Applying Theorem 23 it follows that, if U_2 is preassigned, U_1 may be chosen so that $\gamma = \gamma' + d\alpha_1 + \beta_1$, where α_1 is a singular chain on $V(\lambda) \cap U_2$, β_1 is a singular chain on $V(z_1) \cap U_2$ and γ' is a relative cycle on $V(\lambda, \lambda'') \cap U_2$ modulo $V(z_1, \lambda'') \cap U_2$, λ'' being the sub-arc of λ joining $w_1(z_1)$ and $w_2(z_1)$.

Write $d\gamma' = \mu'$. If λ''' is a sub-arc of λ'' then μ' can be regarded as a representative of an element of $H_{r-1}(V(z_1, \lambda''), V(z_1, \lambda'''))$. Applying around $C_1(z_1)$ and $C_2(z_1)$ the homotopy and excision of Theorem 16, and noting that if the ends of λ''' are sufficiently near those of λ'' then this can be done within a preassigned neighbourhood U_3 such that $U_3 \supset \bar{U}_2$, it follows that $\mu' = \mu_1 + \mu_2 + \mu_3 + d\alpha_2$, where μ_1, μ_2 are relative cycles of $V(z_1, \lambda')$ modulo $V(z_1, \lambda''')$, and are, moreover, singular chains on arbitrary small neighbourhoods M_1, M_2 of $C_1(z_1)$, $C_2(z_1)$, respectively, while μ_3 is a singular chain on $V(z_1, \lambda''') \cap U_3$, and α_2 is a singular chain on $V(z_1, \lambda'') \cap U_3$.

Assume M_1 and M_2 to be as at the beginning of §3, and let $\Delta_1^{*(r-1)}$, $\Delta_2^{*(r-1)}$ be the singular chains induced by f_1, f_2 acting on $\Delta_0^{(r-1)}$. If M_1', M_2' are preassigned neighbourhoods of $C_1(z_1)$, $C_2(z_1)$, respectively, both contained in U_3, then M_1, M_2

may be chosen so that $\mu' = c_1\Delta_1^{*(r-1)} + c_2\Delta_2^{*(r-1)} + \mu_4 + d\alpha_3$
for integers c_1, c_2, where μ_4 is a singular chain on $V(z_1, \lambda''') \cap U_3$
and α_3 is a singular chain on $V(z_1, \lambda'') \cap U_3$. (Induction
Hypothesis, and Theorem 16.)

Now the reasoning of §3 shows that, if U_4 is a preassigned
neighbourhood of C' and U_3 is suitably chosen, then the
addition of suitable chains to $\Delta_1^{*(r-1)}$, $\Delta_2^{*(r-1)}$ yields $\Delta_1^{(r-1)}$,
$\Delta_2^{(r-1)}$, both chains contained in U_4. The chain ν of §3 will
also be in U_4. Thus $\mu' = c_1\Delta_1^{(r-1)} + c_2(\Delta_2^{(r-1)} + \nu) + \mu_5 + d\alpha_3$,
where μ_5 is a singular chain on $V(z_1, \lambda''') \cap U_4$.

At this stage the argument of §3 can be completed by showing
that $\Delta_3'^{(r-1)}$ is homologous to $k'\Delta_1^{(r-1)}$ in the relative homology
of $V(z_1, \lambda')$ modulo $V(z_1, w')$, in a given neighbourhood of C'.
To do this the argument of this section up to this point is to
be repeated, with μ' replaced by $\Delta_3'^{(r-1)}$, noting that only
$\Delta_1^{(r-1)}$ will be involved.

Returning now to the main argument of this section, take boun-
daries in the relation $\mu' = c_1\Delta_1^{(r-1)} + c_2(\Delta_2^{(r-1)} + \nu) + \mu_5 + d\alpha_3$,
noting that $\Delta_1^{(r-1)} + \Delta_2^{(r-1)} + \nu$ is a cycle. Then $(c_1 - c_2)\delta_1^{(r-2)} + d\mu_5$
$= 0$, i.e. $(c_1 - c_2)\delta_1^{(r-2)} \sim 0$ in a $V(z_1, \lambda''') \cap U_4$, and so, if U_4
is suitably chosen, $(c_1 - c_2)\delta_1^{(r-2)} \sim 0$ in $V(z_1, w') \cap U_5$
for a preassigned neighbourhood U_5 of C' (Theorem 24).
But, by Theorem 27 along with the fact that $\delta_1^{(r-2)} \sim \pm\delta_3^{(r-2)}$
in a preassigned neighbourhood of C' if U_5 is small enough,
this implies $c_1 = c_2$. Hence $\mu_1' = c\delta^{(r-1)} + \mu_5 + d\alpha_3$ for some
integer c.

Taking boundaries it follows that μ_5 is a cycle on $V(z_1, \lambda''') \cap U_5$.
If U_5 is small enough and U_6 is a given neighbourhood of
C', μ_5 will be homologous to a cycle μ_6 in $V(z_1, w_1(z_1)) \cap U_6$
(Corollary to Theorem 24, deforming λ'' so that λ''' is carried into
$w_1(z_1)$). It may be assumed that $V'(w_1(z_1)) \cap U_6$ is homologically
trivial, and finally Theorem 12 may be applied to show that,
if U_6 is small enough, then $\mu_6 \sim 0$ in $V(z_1, w_1(z_1)) \cap U_7$ where
U_7 is a preassigned neighbourhood of C'.

Hence $\mu_5 \sim 0$ in $V(z_1) \cap U_7$, and so $\mu' = c\delta^{(r-1)} + d\alpha_4$
where α_4 is a singular chain on $V(z_1) \cap U_7$. $\mu' = c\delta^{(r-1)} + d\alpha_4$
can be written as $d(\gamma' - c\Delta^{(r)} - \alpha_4) = 0$. Thus $\gamma' - c\Delta^{(r)} - \alpha_4$

is a cycle on U_7, which may be assumed to be homologically trivial. It follows at once that $\gamma' \sim c\Delta^{(r)}$ modulo $V(z_1)$, the homology holding in U_7.

As pointed out in Theorem 28, part (1), all that remains to be done in order to verify parts (1) and (2) of Theorem 19 is to show that a relation $c\bar{\Delta}^{(r)} = 0$ implies $c = 0$. Suppose then that $c\bar{\Delta}^{(r)} = 0$ for some integer c. It would follow (Theorem 16) that $c\Delta^{(r)}$ is homologous to zero in $V(\lambda)$ modulo $V(z_1)$ in a preassigned neighbourhood of C', and so $c\delta^{(r-1)}$ would be homologous to zero in $V(z_1) \cap U$, for a preassigned neighbourhood U of C'. If U' is a preassigned neighbourhood of C' and U is small enough, this means $c\delta^{(r-1)} \sim 0$ in $V(z_1, \lambda') \cap U'$ (Theorem 23). Then since $\delta^{(r-1)} = \Delta_1^{(r-1)} + \Delta_2^{(r-1)} + \nu$, and since $(V(z_1, \lambda'); V(z_1, \lambda_1), V(z_1, \lambda_2))$ is a proper triad (Eilenberg and Steenrod [4]), it would follow that $c\Delta_1^{(r-1)}$ and $c\Delta_2^{(r-1)}$ are both homologous to zero modulo $V(z_1, w')$, contrary to the Induction Hypothesis.

To establish part (3) of Theorem 19 let f and f' be two mappings of (E^r, S^{r-1}) into $(V(\lambda), V_0)$ such that $f_* \bar{\Delta}_0^{(r)} = \bar{\Delta}^{(r)}$ and $f'_* \bar{\Delta}_0^{(r)} = \bar{\Delta}'^{(r)}$ are both generators of $H_r(V(\lambda), V_0)$. Assume further that f, f' have their images in a neighbourhood U' of C'. It is to be shown (cf. Theorem 28) that U' can be chosen so that the maps f, f' of (E^r, S^{r-1}) into $(U, V_0 \cap U)$ are homotopic, where U is a preassigned neighbourhood of C'. It is not hard to see that this will follow if the restrictions of f and f' to S^{r-1} are homotopic maps into $V_0 \cap U$, for U may be chosen to be an open cell. Now if $\Delta^{(r)}, \Delta'^{(r)}$ are representatives of $\bar{\Delta}^{(r)}, \bar{\Delta}'^{(r)}$, respectively, obtained by applying f, f' to a representative $\Delta_0^{(r)}$ of $\bar{\Delta}_0^{(r)}$, then, given U, U' can be chosen so that $\Delta'^{(r)}$ and $\Delta^{(r)}$ are homologous (with a suitable choice of sign) in the relative homology of U modulo $U \cap V_0$ (Part (1) of Theorem 19, along with Theorem 16). If $\delta^{(r-1)} = d\Delta^{(r)}, \delta'^{(r-1)} = d\Delta'^{(r)}$ this implies $\delta^{(r-1)} \sim \delta'^{(r-1)}$ in $V_0 \cap U$. Thus the required result will be obtained by a suitable modification of the Hurewicz isomorphism theorem (cf. Hu [8]). As a number of auxiliary results are needed, a separate section will be devoted to this task.

5. Proof of Theorem 19, part (3)

In the first place, noting that the set W of Theorem 16 can be made arbitrarily small, and that, given W, a neighbourhood U' of C' can be found contained in W (by Lemma e, §2, Chapter II) it follows that (by Theorems 16 and 17):

LEMMA a. *If U is a given neighbourhood of C', there exists a neighbourhood U' of C' such that the image of the injection map $H_q(V(\lambda) \cap U', V_0 \cap U') \to H_q(V(\lambda) \cap U, V_0 \cap U)$ is zero for $q \leqslant r - 1$, z_0 being suitably chosen on λ.*

It follows at once from this result that:

LEMMA b. *If U is a given neighbourhood of C', there is a neighbourhood U' of C' such that the image of the injection map $H_q(V_0 \cap U') \to H_q(V_0 \cap U)$ is zero for $q \leqslant r - 2$, z_0 being suitably chosen on λ.*

The main result of this section is the following:

THEOREM 29. **(a)** *If U is a given neighbourhood of C', there a neighbourhood U' of C' and a point z_0 on λ such that the image of the injection map $\pi_q(U' \cap V_0) \to \pi_q(U \cap V_0)$ is zero for $q \leqslant r - 2$.*

(b) *If U is a given neighbourhood of C', there is a neighbourhood of U' of C' and a point $z_0 \in \lambda$ such that if $f : S^{r-1} \to U' \cap V_0$ has the property that the induced homomorphism $f_* : H_{r-1}(S^{r-1}) \to H_{r-1}(U' \cap V_0)$ has zero image, then f, as a mapping into $U \cap V_0$, is homotopic to zero.*

PROOF. In part (a) of this theorem it is understood that the base point for the homotopy groups is some point $y \in U' \cap V_0$. Part (b) is actually the result wanted, but part (a) is required in its proof. The proof of Part (a) is to be inductive, and will be preceded by a discussion of the lower dimensional cases.

In the first place, if $r = 1$, part (a) is meaningless, and part (b) is obviously true; for $V_0 \cap U$ will consist of just two points if U is small enough and f_* has zero image if and only if f maps the sphere S^0 (two points) into a single point, which makes f homotopic to zero trivially.

Secondly put $r = 2$. V_0 is now a curve, and $w_1(z_0)$, $w_2(z_0)$ are clearly two of its branch points over the plane of the complex variable w, and $C_1(z_0)$ and $C_2(z_0)$ are the two points of the curve at which the branching in question takes place. $V(z_0, w')$ consists of a finite set of points, exactly of two which, say P_1 and P_2 lie in U if U is small enough. Now there are well defined arcs $P_i C_j(z_0)$, $(i, j = 1, 2)$ in V_0 lying over λ' and so it follows that $U \cap V(z_0, \lambda'')$ is a homeomorph of a circle, λ'' being the arc on λ' which joins $(z_0, w_1(z_0))$ to $(z_0, w_2(z_0))$. Now let U be a given neighbourhood of C'; U may as well be taken so that $U \cap V(z_0, \lambda'')$ is a homeomorph of a circle. Then, by Theorem 23 there is a neighbourhood U' of C' such that any point of $U' \cap V_0$ can be joined by an arc in $U \cap V_0$ to a point of $U \cap V(z_0, \lambda'')$. Thus any pair of points of $U' \cap V_0$ may be joined by an arc in $U \cap V_0$, which proves part (a) of the theorem for $r = 2$, $q = 0$.

To prove (b) for $r = 2$, suppose $f : S^1 \to U' \cap V_0$ is given so that the induced map $f_* : H_1(S^1) \to H_1(V_0 \cap U')$ has zero image, for some choice of U' and z_0. If U' and z_0 are suitably chosen, Theorem 23 shows that f is homotopic in $U \cap V_0$ to a map $f' : S^1 \to U \cap V(z_0, \lambda'')$ such that the image under f' of a fundamental cycle of S^1 is homologous to zero in $U \cap V(z_0, \lambda'')$. This cannot happen unless f', as a map into the homeomorph of a circle $U \cap V(z_0, \lambda'')$, is homotopic to zero.

Part (a) will now be proved for all values of $r \geqslant 3$ and $q = 0$ or 1. Let U be a given neighbourhood of C' and let U' be as in Lemma b. Then if P and Q are two points of $U' \cap V_0$ the zero dimensional cycle $P - Q$ is homologous to zero in $U \cap V_0$; that is P and Q can be joined by an arc in $U \cap V_0$, which establishes part (a) for $r \geqslant 3$, $q = 0$. To prove Part (a) for $q = 1$ and $r \geqslant 3$, a sequence of neighbourhoods U_i, with $U_i \subset U_{i+1}$ is to be constructed, in a manner similar to the constructions of §§3, 4. Let f be a map of S^1 into $U_1 \cap V_0$ carrying a certain point $x \in S^1$ into a point $y \in V(z_0, \lambda'') \cap U'$, λ'' being the arc on λ' joining $(z_0, w_1(z_0))$ and $(z_0, w_2(z_0))$. Let U_1 and U_2 play the parts of U_1 and U in Theorem 23. Then $f : S' \to U_2 \cap V_0$ is homotopic to a map f' which carries S^1 entirely into $V(z_0, \lambda'') \cap U_2$. The continuity of f' implies that f'^{-1} acting on any closed set gives a closed, and so compact set on S^1. Now let $M_i'' \subset \bar{M}_i'' \subset M_i' \subset M_i$ be neighbourhoods of $C_i(z_0)$ $(i = 1, 2)$ in V_0. The compactness of $\overset{-1}{f'}(\bar{M}_i'')$ and the continuity of f' imply that $\overset{-1}{f'}(\bar{M}_i'')$ may be covered by a finite number of intervals mapped by f' into M_i'. It follows easily that S^1 may be split into a finite number of arcs of three types. Those of the first and second types are mapped by f' into M_1' and M_2' respectively, while those of the third type are mapped into sets not meeting $\bar{M}_1''$ or $\bar{M}_2''$. Let A be an arc of the first type, say, p, q its end points and $P = f'(p), Q = f'(q)$. It is clear that w_1 may be chosen on λ'' so close to $w_1(z_0)$ that P and Q may be joined in M_1' to points P', Q' respectively on $V(z_0, w_1)$; w_1 may be chosen with respect to all the arcs of the first kind, since there is only a finite number of them. Then since part (a) of the present theorem holds for $r \geqslant 2, q = 0$, it follows that, M_1 being preassigned, M_1' can be assumed to be such that P', Q' can be joined by an arc α in $V(z_0, w_1) \cap M_1$, and likewise for all other arcs of the first kind. Assume in addition that $M_1 \subset U_2$ and that M_1 is an $(r - 1)$-cell. Then $f'(A)$ is homotopic to α, the homotopy being carried out entirely in M_1, and so in $V_0 \cap U_2$. This process is to be carried out for all the arcs of the first and the second kinds, the result being that f' is homotopic in $V_0 \cap U_2$ to a map f'' whose image does not meet the M_i''. Then if U_2 and U_3 play the parts of U_1 and U in Theorem 23 it may be assumed that the homotopy from f' to f'' is carried out in $V(z_0, \lambda'') \cap U_3$. Let $\bar{U}_3 \subset U_4$. Then it may be assumed that w_1, selected above, and a similarly selected w_2 are also such that f'' is homotopic in $V(z_0, \lambda'') \cap U_4$ to a map whose image is contained in $V(z_0, \lambda''') \cap U_4$, where λ''' is the join of w_1 and w_2 on λ'. Now apply Theorem 24, U_4 and U_5 playing the parts of U' and U, and the relevant homotopy being that on λ'' which shrinks λ''' to the point $w_1(z_0)$.

Hence f' is homotopic on $V_0 \cap U_5$ to a map whose image lies in $V(z_0, w_1(z_0)) \cap U_5$. Assume further that $V'(w_1(z_0)) \cap U_5$ is an open $(r - 1)$-cell, which is always possible, and finally shrink this cell by Theorem 12 (applied in $V'(w_1(z_0))$) onto $V(z_0, w_1(z_0))$ which can be done in U_6 if U_5 is suitably chosen. The final result is that f', and so f, is homotopic to zero in $U_6 \cap V_0$. This homotopy is a free homotopy, but its existence establishes the existence of a homotopy throughout which x is mapped on the selected base point y. This completes the proof of part (a) for all $r \geqslant 3$ and $q = 1$.

Part (a) will now be proved in general. In view of what has been already proved, attention may be confined to the cases $r \geqslant 4$, $q \geqslant 2$. The result will be proved by induction, the basis of the induction being the already established result for $q = 1$. Let U be a given neighbourhood of C', and $U_1 \subset U_2 \subset U$ where U_1, U_2 are neighbourhoods of C' to be more fully specified presently. Let $f : S^q \to V_0 \cap U_1$ be a map carrying the south pole of S^q into some point $y \in V_0 \cap U_1$, to be fixed from now on. f carries a fundamental cycle of S^q into a q-cycle, which, if U_1 is chosen correctly with respect to U_2, is homologous to zero in $V_0 \cap U_2$ by Lemma b. Hence f may be extended to a polyhedron P^{q+1} which has S^q (suitably triangulated) as its frontier, the extended f carrying P^{q+1} into $V_0 \cap U_2$. A step by step argument, using the hypothesis that part (a) of the theorem holds for maps of 0-, 1-, 2-, ..., $(q-1)$-spheres, shows that if U_2 is suitably chosen the extended map f is homotopic to a map f' which carries the $(q-1)$-skeleton of P^{q+1} into the point y, the homotopy being carried out in $U \cap V_0$. Now let $T_1, \ldots, T_h$ be the q-simplices of P^{q+1}. The map f' and T_i determines, for each i, an element of $\pi_q(U \cap V_0)$, based on y; call this element (f', T_i). And the mapping assigning to each integral chain $\sum a_i T_i$ on P^{q+1} the element $\sum a_i(f', T_i)$ is a homomorphism $\mu : C_q(P^{q+1}) \to \pi_q(U \cap V_0)$, such that μ carries bounding chains into zero (cf. Hu [8]). In particular if α is the fundamental cycle of the triangulated S^q, $\mu(\alpha)$ is the class of the map $f : S^q \to U \cap V_0$, but α is a boundary and so f is homotopic to zero in $U \cap V_0$.

Part (a) is now completely proved. Part (b) is proved for $r \geqslant 3$ by the same argument as has just been carried out, with q replaced by $r - 1$. The essential point of making the map f' carry the $r - 2$ skeleton into a point y is established by applying the already proved part (a) of the theorem.

Theorem 29 will now be applied to finish off the argument of §4. U being a given neighbourhood of C' let U_1 and U play the parts of U' and U in Theorem 29, part (b). Let U_2 and U_1 play the parts of U' and U of Lemma b, and let U' be a neighbourhood of C' such that any pair of points of $U' \cap V_0$ may be joined by an arc in $U_2 \cap V_0$ (Theorem 29 part (a) for $q = 0$). Then if x is the south pole of S^{r-1}, $f(x)$ and $f'(x)$ may be joined to a point $y \in U_2 \cap V_0$ by arcs in $U_2 \cap V_0$, f and f' being the maps introduced at the end of §4. Then it follows that f and f' are respectively homotopic to maps f_1 and f_1' of S^{r-1} into $V_0 \cap U_2$, carrying x into the selected point y, the homotopy being carried out in $V_0 \cap U_2$. f_1 and f_1' represent elements of $\pi_{r-1}(V_0 \cap U)$ in the image of the injection of $\pi_{r-1}(V_0 \cap U_2)$. The difference map $f_1 - f_1'$ may be constructed and is a map which, by Lemma b applied to U_1 and U_2, carries a fundamental cycle of S^{r-1} into a cycle homologous to zero in $V_0 \cap U_1$. Then by Theorem 29 (b), f_1 and f_1', and so f and f' are homotopic in $U \cap V_0$.

This completes the verifications of the various parts of the Theorem 19 for dimension r, and so completes the induction, thus proving that theorem.

CHAPTER VI

THE POINCARÉ FORMULA

1. The automorphisms T_i

As before let $z_1, \ldots, z_k$ be the parameters of the singular sections of V by the pencil Π, and let K denote the complex sphere S with these points removed. As shown in §3, Chapter I, there is a fibre bundle X with base K and some non-singular section V_0 of V as typical fibre, also that X contains a sub-bundle X' equivalent to $K \times P$ each fibre of X' being contained in the corresponding fibre of X. Moreover (Theorem 4) there is a continuous mapping $\psi \colon X \to V(K)$ which is homeomorphic on $X - X'$, mapping this set onto $V(K) - P$. If V_0 is the section of V of paramenter z_0 and X_0 is the fibre of X over the base point z_0, then ψ restricted to X_0 induces a homeomorphism ψ_0 of the pair $(X_0, X_0') = (X_0, X_0 \cap X')$ onto the pair (V_0, P).

The covering homotopy theorem for fibre bundles and the standard methods of discussing the homology of such spaces may now be adapted to show that the fundamental group of K acts as a group of automorphisms on $H_q(X_0, X_0')$ for each q. If S_α is the automorphism corresponding to the element $\alpha \in \pi_1(K)$ and $\psi_{0*} \colon H_q(X_0, X_0') \to H_q(V_0, P)$ is induced by the homeomorphism ψ_0, then $T_\alpha = \psi_{0*} \, S \, \psi_{\alpha 0*}^{-1}$ is a well defined automorphism of $H_q(V_0, P)$. Moreover the fibre bundle theory gives a method of computing the effect of the operators S_α, and so T_α. Namely, denote by α a representative path in the class $\alpha \in \pi_1(K)$ and let σ be a singular simplex of dimension q on V_0, that is to say a continuous mapping of a Euclidean simplex Δ into V_0. Then there is a homotopy $F \colon \Delta \times I \to V(K)$ covering α such that F coincides with σ on $\Delta \times \{0\}$ and $F(\Delta \times \{1\}) \subset V_0$. F restricted to $\Delta \times \{1\}$ is defined as $T_\alpha(\sigma)$. T_α is constructed for different singular simplexes in such a way that cycles are carried into cycles, and boundaries into boundaries. Also simplexes on P are carried into simplexes on P. It follows at once that T_α induces an automorphism on $H_q(V_0, P)$, as required.

This chapter will be occupied with the application of this method to the computation of $T_\alpha(\bar{\gamma})$ for certain basic α and $\bar{\gamma}$, and for $q = r - 1$.

Let the paths λ_i from an ordinary point z_0 on S to the special points z_i be constructed as in §3, Chapter III. Let α_i be a path starting at z_0, going along λ_i until close to z_i, going once round z_i counterclockwise (round a circle say, small enough not to contain any z_j for $j \neq i$) and back to z_0 along λ_i. $\pi_1(K)$ is generated by the homotopy classes of the α_i. Write $T_i = T_{\alpha_i}$. Then the $T_i(i = 1, 2, \ldots, k)$ generate the group of automorphisms on $H_q(V_0, P)$ induced by $\pi_1(K)$ for each q.

Attention will now be fixed on one particular value of i, and the automorphism T_i will be examined in greater detail. As usual it is convenient to change the notation, taking $V(z')$ as the singular section to be considered, λ as a path from z' to z_0, C' the singular point on $V(z')$ and T for the corresponding automorphism on $H_q(V_0, P)$. It is also convenient for the present purpose to take z_0 close to z'; just how close will be made more explicit presently.

THEOREM 30. T *acts as the identity on* $H_q(V_0, P)$ *for* $q \leqslant r - 2$.

PROOF. For if $\bar{\gamma} \in H_q(V_0, P)$ then $T(\bar{\gamma}) - \bar{\gamma}$ is in the kernel of the injection $H_q(V_0, P) \to H_q(V, P)$, and so in the image of the boundary homomorphism $\partial : H_{q+1}(V, V_0) \to H_q(V_0, P)$. But $H_{q+1}(V, V_0) = 0$ for $q \leqslant r - 2$ (Theorem 17) and so $T(\bar{\gamma}) = \bar{\gamma}$.

THEOREM 31. *Let* $\bar{\gamma} \in H_{r-1}(V_0, P)$, δ *generate the kernel of the injection* $H_{r-1}(V_0, P) \to H_{r-1}(V(\lambda), P)$, γ, δ *representatives of* $\bar{\gamma}, \delta$ *respectively,* δ *being a singular cycle on some neighbourhood of* C' *not meeting* P. *Then there is an integer* c (*independent of* $\bar{\gamma}$) *such that* $T(\bar{\gamma}) = \bar{\gamma} + c(\gamma . \delta)\delta$, *where* $(\gamma . \delta)$ *is the intersection number of* γ *and* δ.

Before getting started on the proof note that δ can be constructed so as to lie in a set not meeting P (§3, Chapter V), and also that, being constructed in this way, δ is a cycle not meeting the boundary of γ, and hence that the intersection number $(\gamma \cdot \delta)$ is well defined.

Next, V_0 is a differentiable manifold, P a submanifold, and so there exists a triangulation of V_0 making it into a simplicial complex with P as a subcomplex. It follows that any element of $H_{r-1}(V_0, P)$ can always be represented by a simplicial chain, and any homology can always be written as a simplicial homology.

PROOF OF THEOREM 31. To prove the theorem T may be supposed to be induced by an element of $\pi_1(K)$ represented by a single counter-clockwise circuit of a small circle about z', say the circumference D of a small circular neighbourhood N of z' whose closure does not contain the parameter of any other singular section of V. Then $T(\bar{\gamma}) - \bar{\gamma}$ is clearly in the kernel of the injection $H_{r-1}(V_0, P) \to H_{r-1}(V(\bar{N}), P)$, and so, since the pair $(V(\lambda), P)$ is a deformation retract of $(V(\bar{N}), P)$ (Theorem 12) also in the kernel of the injection $H_{r-1}(V_0, P) \to H_{r-1}(V(\lambda), P)$. Thus $T(\bar{\gamma}) - \bar{\gamma} = \bar{f}_1(\bar{\gamma})\delta$, where $\bar{f}_1$ is an integer valued function of $\bar{\gamma}$. If $\delta = 0$ there is no more to be said. Otherwise write $f_1(\gamma) = \bar{f}_1(\bar{\gamma})$ for any simplicial representative γ of $\bar{\gamma}$. The function f_1 so defined is now to be extended to the whole group $C_{r-1}(V_0)$ of simplicial $(r-1)$-chains on V_0.

Using now the notation of §1, Chapter II, let F be the family of radii of N. The conditions on F stated there are satisfied with K and E replaced by N and z' respectively. Construct the family of curves F' as in Chapter II. Let U be an open neighbourhood of C', and let W_1 be the set of all points on all curves of F' ending in U. Write $W_2 = V(\bar{N}) - W_1$. Lemmas e and f, §2, Chapter II, show that W_1 is open in $V(\bar{N})$, and moreover can be made to lie in a preassigned neighbourhood of C' if U is made small enough. Also it is clear that $V_0 \cap W_2$ is a deformation retract of W_2, and so, if $\bar{\gamma} \in H_{r-1}(V_0, P)$ has a representative γ which is a simplicial chain on $W_2 \cap V_0$, it follows that $T(\bar{\gamma}) = \bar{\gamma}$, and this, along with the assumption that $\delta \neq 0$, implies that $f_1(\gamma) = 0$.

Define now the linear function f on $C_{r-1}(V_0)$:

(1) If $\gamma \in C_{r-1}(V_0)$ is a relative cycle modulo P, set $f(\gamma) = f_1(\gamma)$.

(2) If $\gamma \in C_{r-1}(W_2 \cap V_0)$, set $f(\gamma) = 0$.

By the remark just made above, if $\gamma \in C_{r-1}(W_2 \cap V_0)$ and also is a relative cycle modulo P, $f_1(\gamma) = 0$, and so (1) and (2) agree. The linear function f is thus fully defined on the subgroup $Z_{r-1}(V_0, P) + C_{r-1}(W_2 \cap V_0)$ of $C_{r-1}(V_0)$, Z denoting the group of relative cycles. Let π be the natural homomorphism $C_{r-2}(V_0) \to C_{r-2}(V_0, P) = C_{r-2}(V_0)/C_{r-2}(P)$, and d the boundary operator $d : C_{r-1}(V_0, P) \to C_{r-2}(V_0, P)$. Then $Z_{r-1}(V_0, P)$ is the kernel of $\pi \circ d$. Since $Z_{r-1}(V_0, W_2 \cap V_0)$ is a subgroup of $C_{r-1}(V_0)$ containing $Z_{r-1}(V_0, P)$, the map $\pi \circ d$ carries $Z_{r-1}(V_0, W_2 \cap V_0)$ onto a subgroup of $C_{r-2}(V_0, P)$ and the restriction of $\pi \circ d$ to $Z_{r-1}(V_0, W_2 \cap V_0)$ has kernel $Z_{r-1}(V_0, P)$. Thus $Z_{r-1}(V_0, W_2 \cap V_0)/Z_{r-1}(V_0, P)$ is isomorphic to a subgroup of the free group $C_{r-2}(V_0, P)$ and so is free. Thus $Z_{r-1}(V_0, P)$ is a direct summand in $Z_{r-1}(V_0, W_2 \cap V_0)$. Write $Z_{r-1}(V_0, W_2 \cap V_0) = Z_{r-1}(V_0, P) \dotplus G$, and extend f to $Z_{r-1}(V_0, W_2 \cap V_0)$ by setting it equal to zero on G. This extension involves no contradiction. For f is already defined on

$$
\begin{aligned}
Z_{r-1}&(V_0, P) + C_{r-1}(W_2 \cap V_0) \\
&= Z_{r-1}(V_0, P) + C_{r-1}(W_2 \cap V_0) \cap Z_{r-1}(V_0, P) \\
&\qquad + C_{r-1}(W_2 \cap V_0) \cap G \\
&= Z_{r-1}(V_0, P) \dotplus C_{r-1}(W_2 \cap V_0) \cap G
\end{aligned}
$$

(the last summation being direct) and the value so far given for f on the subgroup $C_{r-1}(W_2 \cap V_0) \cap G$ of G is zero. Continuing the argument, $Z_{r-1}(V_0, W_2 \cap V_0)$ is a direct summand of $C_{r-1}(V_0)$, since $C_{r-1}(V_0)/Z_{r-1}(V_0, W_2 \cap V_0)$ is isomorphic to a subgroup of $C_{r-2}(V_0, W_2 \cap V_0)$ and so is free. Hence f may be extended to the whole group $C_{r-1}(V_0)$ as required.

Thus f is an integral valued simplicial cochain on V_0. It is also, however, a cocycle. For $f(d\beta)$, where β is an r-chain on V_0, and d is the boundary operator, is given by the definition

(1) above: $f(d\beta) = f_1(d\beta)$. But $d\beta$ is homologous to zero on V_0 and so on V_0 modulo P, and so $T(\overline{d\beta}) = \overline{d\beta} = 0$, and so, since δ is assumed at present to be non-zero, $f_1(d\beta) = 0$. But a simplicial cocycle can always be represented by means of a cycle in the dual simplicial subdivision. That is to say, there is a cycle γ_0 of the dual subdivision such that for any simplicial chain γ, $f(\gamma) = (\gamma \cdot \gamma_0)$, the intersection number. Also f has been so defined as to vanish on any simplex which does not meet W_1. Now W_1 can be constructed to lie in U_0 where U_0 is a preassigned neighbourhood of C', (Lemma f, §2, Chapter II) and so if the triangulation of V_0, and the dual subdivision, are made fine enough, γ_0 will be composed of simplexes lying entirely in U_0. If U_0 is chosen so as to be homologically trivial it will follow that γ_0 represents an element of the kernel of the injection $H_{r-1}(V_0, P) \to H_{r-1}(V(\overline{N}), P)$, and so is homologous in V_0 modulo P to an integral multiple of the appropriate "vanishing cycle". That is to say, using the usual convention for the intersection numbers of singular chains $f(\gamma) = c(\gamma \cdot \delta)$ for some integer, c, where γ need no longer be simplicial, but may be any singular representative of $\bar{\gamma}$.

The formula $T(\bar{\gamma}) = \bar{\gamma} + c(\gamma \cdot \delta)\bar{\delta}$ is thus established; the next task is to show that c is in fact equal to -1. This will be done by selecting a particular element to take the place of $\bar{\gamma}$, an element for which $T(\bar{\gamma})$ may be calculated in a different way. Also the intersection number $(\gamma \cdot \delta)$ will be computed for this particular γ, and the two different evaluations for $T(\bar{\gamma})$ will be compared. The question of evaluating c only arises, of course, when $\delta \neq 0$. And until further notice this assumption, that $\delta \neq 0$, will be made.

2. Explicit calculation of T

The integer c appearing in Theorem 31 must now be calculated. The method will be to apply Theorem 31 to an element $\bar{\gamma}$ of $H_{r-1}(V_0, P)$ for which $T(\bar{\gamma})$ and the intersection number $(\gamma \cdot \delta)$ can be calculated independently. As part of this working is rather elaborate, the details of the proofs of the theorems involved will be postponed till Chapter VII, and in the meantime a geometrical sketch of the argument will be given.

It will be remembered that, by Theorem 19 applied to V_0, a set of generators for $H_{r-1}(V_0, P)$ can be obtained such that one generator is associated with each singular section $V(z_0, w_i)$ of V_0 by a hyperplane of Π'; the understanding is that each point w_i involved is joined by an arc μ_i to the point ∞ in the complex w-plane, and the ith generator is represented by a relative cycle of $V(z_0, \mu_i)$ modulo P. In particular, using the notation of §3, Chapter IV, there are two values of w, namely $w_1(z)$ and $w_2(z)$ for each z near z' such that $V(z, w_1(z))$ and $V(z, w_2(z))$ are singular sections of $V(z)$. The effect of T will now be studied on the generator of $H_{r-1}(V_0, P)$ associated as just indicated with $V(z_0, w_1(z_0))$. But first, suitable arcs joining $w_1(z_0)$ and $w_2(z_0)$ to ∞ on the complex w-plane must be constructed. The following is a convenient construction for this purpose.

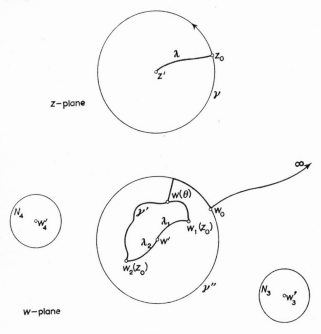

Fig. 1

Apart from (z', w'), the line $z = z'$ in the (z, w)-plane meets the curve Γ in a finite number of points with w-coordinates $w_3', w_4', \ldots, w_s'$, say. These are all finite since, by the way coordinates have been chosen, the axis of Π corresponds to $w = \infty$.

Let $N_0, N_3, \ldots, N_s$ be neighbourhoods of $w', w_3, \ldots, w_s'$, respectively, on the complex w-plane no two of which intersect. Then, for z_1 sufficiently near z', the line $z = z_1$ will have s intersections with Γ two of which, $(z_1, w_1(z_1))$, $(z_1, w_2(z_1))$ have their w-coordinates in N_0, while of the w coordinates of the remaining intersections, one lies in each of $N_3, \ldots, N_s$.

Fix attention for a moment on $w_1(z)$, $w_2(z)$, for values of z near z'. The two valued function $w(z)$ with values $w_1(z)$, $w_2(z)$, is given around z' by a quadratic equation

$$(w - w')^2 + p(z)(w - w') + q(z) = 0,$$

where $p(z)$, $q(z)$ are analytic around z' and both vanish at z'. The requirement that Γ should have a well defined tangent at (z', w') implies that $dq/dz \neq 0$ at $z = z'$. It follows that $w(z)$ may be expanded in a series of the form $w' + c_1\sqrt{z - z'} + c_2(z - z') + \ldots$, where $c_1 \neq 0$. That is to say $w(z) = w' + (c_1 + \eta) \sqrt{z - z'}$, where $|\eta| < k|\sqrt{z - z'}|$, k being a certain constant, provided $|z - z'|$ is sufficiently small.

Now assume that N is a circular neighbourhood of radius ρ about z', such that $k\sqrt{\rho} < \frac{1}{4}|c_1|$, such that a circle about w' in the w-plane of radius $\frac{5}{4}|c_1|\sqrt{\rho}$ is contained in N_0, and such that the points of Γ with coordinates (z, w), $z \in N$, apart from $(z, w_1(z))$, $(z, w_2(z))$ have their w coordinates lying one in each of $N_3, \ldots, N_s$. Then as z traces the circumference γ of N, starting and finishing at z_0, the two values $w_1^*(z)$, $w_2^*(z)$ of the function $w^*(z) = w' + c_1\sqrt{z - z'}$ trace out semicircles about w' of radius $|c_1|\sqrt{\rho}$ in the w-plane. And the paths of $w_1(z)$, $w_2(z)$ approximate these semicircles. More specifically for $i = 1, 2$, the distance of $w_i(z)$ from $w_i^*(z)$ is

$$|\eta| |\sqrt{z - z'}| < k\rho < \frac{1}{4}|c_1|\sqrt{\rho}.$$

Starting with the value $w_1(z_0)$ it thus follows that, as $z(\theta) = z' + \rho e^{i\theta}$ traces out γ from $\theta = \theta_0$ to $\theta = 2\pi + \theta_0$, this particular value of $w(z)$ traces out an arc γ' from $w_1(z_0)$ to $w_2(z_0)$, the moving point of γ' being a function $w(\theta)$ of θ only. Moreover, the arc γ' will lie entirely within a circle γ'' about w' of radius $\frac{5}{4}|c_1|\sqrt{\rho}$, and hence, by the choice of N, entirely within N_0 (cf. Fig. 1, p. 77).

Fix any point w_0 on γ'' and let μ_0 be any path on the w-plane from w_0 to ∞, lying entirely outside γ'', and not meeting the closures of $N_3, \ldots, N_s$. Let $\mu(\theta)$ denote the path from $w(\theta)$ to ∞ obtained by joining $w(\theta)$ to a point of γ'' along a radius of γ'' and then joining this point of γ'' to w_0 by an arc of the circumference of γ'' finally proceeding to ∞ along μ_0.

Then it is not hard to see that, as θ varies from θ_0 (at z_0) to $\theta_0 + 2\pi$, the path $(z(\theta), \mu(\theta))$ in the (z, w)-plane is deformed continuously from its initial position $(z_0, \mu_1) = (z_0, \mu(\theta_0))$ to $(z_0, \mu_2) = (z_0, \mu(\theta_0 + 2\pi))$. The idea is to lift this deformation into V, fibred by its sections with the $(n - 2)$-spaces through L. This is not, however, a straightforward matter of applying the modified covering homotopy theorem (Theorem 5) as the arc $(z(\theta), \mu(\theta))$ always has the special point $(z(\theta), w(\theta))$ on it. But this difficulty may be got around with a little care, and it will be shown that, as (z_0, μ_1) is deformed into (z_0, μ_2), a relative cycle Δ_1 representing a generator of $H_{r-1}(V(z_0, \mu_1), P)$ is carried into a relative cycle Δ_2 representing a generator of $H_{r-1}(V(z_0, \mu_2), P)$. If $\bar{\Delta}_1, \bar{\Delta}_2$, are the relative homology classes of Δ_1, Δ_2 in V_0 modulo P, this implies the following result:

THEOREM 32. $T(\bar{\Delta}_1) = \pm\bar{\Delta}_2$.

The proof of this theorem will be given in §3, Chapter VII.

The chains Δ_1 and Δ_2 just mentioned are to be chosen in rather a special way. It will be noticed, by examining Fig. 1, that $\lambda' = \lambda_1 \cup \lambda_2$ can be deformed into $\mu_1 \cup \mu_2$, leaving $w_1(z_0)$ and $w_2(z_0)$ fixed. It will be shown (Chapter VII) that this deformation can be lifted into a deformation of the two chains $\Delta_1^{(r-1)}, \Delta_2^{(r-1)}$ of §3, Chapter IV or §3, Chapter V (which are, geometrically speaking, hemispheres embedded in V) into two chains which are respectively relative cycles on $V(z_0, \mu_1)$ and $V(z_0, \mu_2)$ modulo P. These two chains are to be taken as Δ_1 and Δ_2.

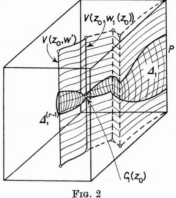

FIG. 2

The formula $T(\bar{\Delta}_1) = \pm \bar{\Delta}_2$ will eventually be compared with the formula $T(\bar{\Delta}_1) = \bar{\Delta}_1 + c(\Delta_1 . \delta)\bar{\delta}$, and, since it is intended to find c in this way, attention will be confined to the case $\bar{\delta} \neq 0$. The first thing to notice is that $\bar{\delta} = \bar{\Delta}_1 + \bar{\Delta}_2$, for in §3, Chapter V, the vanishing cycle δ was constructed as $\Delta_1^{(r-1)} + \Delta_2^{(r-1)} + \nu$ where ν is a chain on $V(z_0, w')$. The deformation of $\Delta_1^{(r-1)}$ and $\Delta_2^{(r-1)}$ into Δ_1 and Δ_2 then shows that δ is homologous to $\Delta_1 + \Delta_2$ modulo P, as asserted. On the other hand, $\Delta_1^{(r-1)} + \Delta_2^{(r-1)} + \nu$ can still be taken as a representative of δ, and so it is not hard to see that $(\Delta_1 . \delta) = (\Delta_1 . \Delta_1^{(r-1)})$, for the point $C_1(z_0)$ is, geometrically speaking, the only point in common of δ and Δ_1; (see Fig. 2).

The next stage is to carry out the explicit calculation of an intersection number of the type $(\Delta_1^{(r-1)} . \Delta_1)$. For this purpose it is convenient to change the notation and to consider the following situation (see Fig. 3, p. 81).

z' is a special point on the z-plane S (with the point ∞) and λ and μ are two piecewise analytic arcs ending at z'. Δ represents a generator of $H_r(V(\lambda), V(z_0))$. λ can be deformed into μ in two essentially different ways, namely clockwise and anti-clockwise. By lifting these deformations into V it will be shown that:

THEOREM 33. *There are two isomorphisms* $T^c_{\mu\lambda}$ *and* $T^a_{\mu\lambda}$ *of* $H_r(V(\lambda), V(z_0))$ *onto* $H_r(V(\mu), V(z'_0))$.

A fuller and more general statement of this theorem will be proved in §1, Chapter VII (Theorem 38).

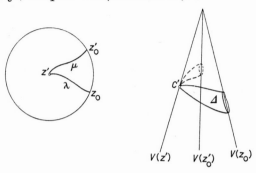

FIG. 3

The object now is to calculate the intersection number $(\Delta \cdot T^a_{\mu\lambda}(\Delta))$. By Theorem 19, Δ and $T^a_{\mu\lambda}(\Delta)$ are images of a relative cycle on E^r modulo S^{r-1} under continuous mappings h_0 and h_1, say, into V. It will be shown that the mappings h_0 and h_1 can be made differentiable and homeomorphic and that the homotopy of h_0 into h_1 which, in fact, defines the operation $T^a_{\mu\lambda}$, can also be made differentiable. It will follow at once that the interesction number $(\Delta \cdot T^a_{\mu\lambda}(\Delta))$ can be computed by examining the configuration of the tangent linear varieties to $h_0(E^r)$ and $h_1(E^r)$ at C'. This will be done in §4, Chapter VII; the result is:

THEOREM 34. $(\Delta \cdot T^a_{\mu\lambda}(\Delta)) = 1$.

3. The formula $T(\bar{\gamma}) = \bar{\gamma} - (\gamma \cdot \delta)\bar{\delta}$. (Poincaré Formula)

Using the intersection formula obtained in Theorem 34, the study of the automorphism T of §1 will be continued. The first step is to find the effect of T on δ, the result being:

THEOREM 35. $T(\delta) = (-1)^r \delta$.

PROOF. λ as usual is to be an arc joining z_0 and z'. Let μ be a second arc obtained from λ by an anticlockwise rotation. By Theorem 33 the three homomorphisms $T^a_{\lambda\lambda}, T^a_{\lambda\mu}, T^a_{\mu\lambda}$ can be constructed, and they satisfy the relation $T^a_{\lambda\lambda} = T^a_{\lambda\mu} T^a_{\mu\lambda}$

(cf. end of §1, Chapter VII). Let Δ represent a generator $\bar{\Delta}$ of $H_r(V(\lambda),\ V_0)$. By Theorem 34, $(\Delta\ .\ T^a_{\mu\lambda}(\Delta)) = 1$. Applying Theorem 34 again to $T^a_{\mu\lambda}(\Delta)$, the result $(T^a_{\mu\lambda}(\Delta)\ .\ T^a_{\lambda\mu}T^a_{\mu\lambda}(\Delta))$ $= 1$ is obtained; that is to say, $(T^a_{\mu\lambda}(\Delta)\ .\ T^a_{\lambda\lambda}(\Delta)) = 1$. But $T^a_{\lambda\lambda}$ is clearly an automorphism of $H_r(V(\lambda),\ V_0)$ and so $T^a_{\lambda\lambda}(\Delta) = k\bar{\Delta}$, where $k = \pm 1$. Hence $k(T^a_{\mu\lambda}(\Delta)\ .\ \Delta) = 1$. But $(T^a_{\mu\lambda}(\Delta)\ .\ \Delta) = (-1)^r(\Delta\ .\ T^a_{\mu\lambda}(\Delta)) = (-1)^r$, and so $k = (-1)^r$. The theorem is then proved by noting that $T(\delta)$ is obtained by applying the boundary homomorphism to the formula $T^a_{\lambda\lambda}(\bar{\Delta}) = (-1)^r\bar{\Delta}$ which has just been proved (cf. Theorem 38).

THEOREM 36. $T(\bar{\Delta}_1) = -\bar{\Delta}_2$.

PROOF. It will be remembered that $\bar{\Delta}_1$ and $\bar{\Delta}_2$, elements of $H_{r-1}(V_0,\ P)$, are represented by relative cycles Δ_1 and Δ_2 in $V(z_0,\ \mu_1)$ and $V(z_0,\ \mu_2)$, respectively. Also $\delta = \bar{\Delta}_1 + \bar{\Delta}_2$ (cf. §2) and δ may be represented by $\Delta_1^{(r-1)} + \Delta_2^{(r-1)} + \nu$ where $\Delta_1^{(r-1)}$ and $\Delta_2^{(r-1)}$ are relative cycles on $V(z_0,\ \lambda_1)$ and $V(z_0,\ \lambda_2)$, respectively, modulo $V(z_0,\ w')$, and ν is a chain in $V(z_0,\ w')$. Then, using the intersection formula of Theorem 34, it follows that $(\Delta_1\ .\ \delta) = (\Delta_1\ .\ \Delta_1^{(r-1)}) = 1$, since the deformation of μ_1 into λ_1 (cf. Fig. 1, p. 77) is anticlockwise, working this time entirely in V_0, parametrizing the pencil of sections $V(z_0,\ w)$ by w. Similarly $(\delta\ .\ \Delta_2) = (\Delta_2^{(r-1)}\ .\ \Delta_2) = 1$.

The automorphism T, however, preserves intersection numbers, and so $(\Delta_1\ .\ \delta) = (T(\Delta_1)\ .\ T(\delta)) = (-1)^rk(\Delta_2\ .\ \delta)$, where $k = \pm 1$ by Theorem 32. Hence $1 = (-1)^rk(\Delta_2\ .\ \delta) = -k(\delta\ .\ \Delta_2) = -k$, and so $k = -1$, as was to be proved.

THEOREM 37. For any element $\bar{\gamma} \in H_{r-1}(V_0,\ P)$, $T(\bar{\gamma}) = \bar{\gamma} - (\gamma\ .\ \delta)\bar{\delta}$, where $\gamma,\ \delta$ are representatives of $\bar{\gamma}$ and $\bar{\delta}$ respectively.

PROOF. It has already been shown that $T(\bar{\gamma}) = \bar{\gamma} + c(\gamma\ .\ \delta)\bar{\delta}$ in Theorem 31. Applying this formula to $\bar{\gamma} = \bar{\Delta}_1$ it follows that $T(\bar{\Delta}_1) = \bar{\Delta}_1 + c(\Delta_1\ .\ \delta)\bar{\delta} = \bar{\Delta}_1 + c(\Delta_1\ .\ \Delta_1^{(r-1)})\bar{\delta} = \bar{\Delta}_1 + c\bar{\delta}$, since $(\Delta_1\ .\ \delta) = (\Delta_1\ .\ \Delta_1^{(r-1)}) = 1$ by Theorem 34. But $T(\bar{\Delta}_1) = -\bar{\Delta}_2$ by Theorem 36, and so $-\bar{\Delta}_2 = \bar{\Delta}_1 + c\bar{\delta}$; that is to say $(c + 1)\bar{\delta} = 0$ and so, since $\bar{\delta} = 0$ has been excluded, $c = -1$, as required.

CHAPTER VII

THE POINCARÉ FORMULA; DETAILS OF PROOF

1. Clockwise and anti-clockwise isomorphisms

It is convenient to start the verifications of the results sketched in Chapter VI by proving Theorem 33, in a slightly more general form.

Let K be a set on the complex z-plane homeomorphic to a closed disc, and let all the points of K be ordinary except one, namely z', to be contained in its interior. Let λ, μ be two arcs in K having no point in common except z', which is to be an end point of both. It will be assumed that λ and μ are both unions of arcs analytically homeomorphic to a closed line segment and that these arcs are joined end to end, no two of them having points in common other than endpoints. Finally it will be assumed that λ and μ have distinct tangents at z'. Then the following is the theorem to be proved:

THEOREM 38. *Associated with each homotopy class α of paths from the end point z_0 of λ to the end point z'_0 of μ, in the sense of homotopy in $K - z'$ with respect to fixed endpoints, there is an isomorphism $T^\alpha_{\mu\lambda}$ of $H_r(V(\lambda), V(z_0))$ onto $H_r(V(\mu), V(z'_0))$ such that, if $T^\alpha : H_{r-1}(V(z_0)) \to H_{r-1}(V(z'_1))$ is the isomorphism induced as in a fibre bundle (cf. also §1, Chapter VI) by the operation of a path of class α in the base (in this case $K - z'$), then the following diagram is commutative:*

$$
\begin{array}{ccc}
H_r(V(\lambda),\ V(z_0)) & \xrightarrow{\ T^\alpha_{\mu\lambda}\ } & H_r(V(\mu),\ V(z'_0)) \\
\Big\downarrow \partial & & \Big\downarrow \partial \\
H_{r-1}(V(z_0)) & \xrightarrow{\ T_\alpha\ } & H_{r-1}(V(z'_0)).
\end{array}
$$

The proof of this theorem will be split up into the following two lemmas.

LEMMA a. *Let α_1 be a path joining z_0 to z_0' in $K - z'$. Then there is a homotopy $F : V(\lambda) \times I \to V(K)$ of the inclusion mapping of $V(\lambda)$ into $V(K)$ with the following properties:*

(1) *F restricted to $V(\lambda) \times \{0\}$ is the inclusion mapping;*

(2) *$F(V(\lambda) \times \{1\}) = V(\mu)$;*

(3) *$F(V(z_0) \times \{t\}) = V(z(t))$, where $z(t)$ is the point of parameter t on α_1.*

PROOF. Let N be a closed circular neighbourhood of z' such that, in N, a family of curves can be constructed with the properties of the family F in §1, Chapter II, K and E being replaced here by N and z', respectively. Assume also that this family of curves includes the parts of λ and μ in N; this can be done if N is small enough because of the assumptions made on λ and μ. Let N_1 be a second circular neighbourhood of z' whose radius is half that of N. Let D be the circumference of N_1 and let λ and μ meet D in z_1 and z_1' respectively; these points are uniquely defined if N_1 is small enough.

Now the fundamental group of $K - z'$ is isomorphic to that of D, under the inclusion mapping, and so the closed path which starts at z_1, goes along the path λ to z_0, along α_1 to z_0', along μ from z_0' to z_1' and finally back to z_1 along D (in either direction) is homotopic in $K - z'$, and in fact in $K - N_1$, to a path lying entirely on D, the homotopy being with respect to the fixed base-point z_1. This statement may be reinterpreted in the following way; namely that there is a deformation of the part of λ joining z_1 to z_0 into a path which consists of a path on D from z_1 to z_1' followed by the part of μ from z_1' to z_0', the point z_1 being fixed throughout the deformation, while z_0 moves along α_1 to z_0'. This deformation can be lifted into V by Theorem 5. Thus, if μ' is the curve formed by the part of λ from z' to z_1, followed by a certain path on D, and then by the part of μ from z_1' to z_0', the statement of this lemma has been proved with μ replaced by μ'. The proof of the lemma is completed by applying Theorem 12, which shows the existence of a homotopy of the identity mapping of $V(N)$ onto itself into a mapping which carries $V(N_1)$ onto $V(z')$. In particular this mapping carries $V(\mu')$ into $V(\mu)$, and the lemma is proved.

LEMMA b. *Continuing with the notation introduced above, let α_0 be a closed path based on z_0 and homotopic to a constant in $K - z'$. Let $F : V(\lambda) \times I \to V(K)$ be a mapping with the following properties:*

(1) $F(V(\lambda) \times \{0\}) = F(V(\lambda) \times \{1\})) = V(\lambda)$;

(2) $F(V(z_0) \times \{t\}) = V(z(t))$, *where $z(t)$ is the point of parameter t on α_0;*

(3) $F(V(\lambda) \times \{t\}) = V(\lambda(t))$, *where $\lambda(t)$ is a path joining z' to $z(t)$, and for each $z \in \lambda$, $F(V(z) \times \{t\}) = V(f(z, t))$, where $f(z, t) \in \lambda(t)$.*

Then, defining F_0 and F_1 as the restrictions of F to $V(\lambda) \times \{0\}$ and $V(\lambda) \times \{1\}$ respectively, the two mappings F_0 and F_1 of $(V(\lambda), V(z_0))$ into itself are homotopic (that is as mappings into $(V(\lambda), V(z_0))$).

PROOF. Condition (3) above implies the existence of a mapping $f : \lambda \times I \to K$ such that $f(\lambda \times \{t\}) = \lambda(t)$. Taking coordinates (s, t) on $\lambda \times I$, the side $s = 0$ is mapped by f into z', the sides $t = 0$ and $t = 1$ into λ, and the side $s = 1$ into α_0. Let N and N_1 be as in the proof of Lemma a, and in addition chosen so small that the path α_0 does not meet $\overline{N}$. Then there is a number s' such that the part of $\lambda \times I$ defined by $s \geqslant s'$ does not meet $f^{-1}(\overline{N})$.

Define the mapping $g : \lambda \times I \times I$ into K as follows:

(1) $g(s, t, u) = f(s, t)$, for all $s \leqslant s'$, u being the parameter on the second copy of I;

(2) $g(1, t, u) = h(t, u)$, where h is a mapping of $I \times I$ into $K - \overline{N}$ such that $h(t, 0) = z(t), h(t, 1) = z_0, h(0, u) = h(1, u) = z_0$ for all u. Such a mapping h exists since α_0 is homotopic to a constant in $K - z'$, and so in $K - N$ if $\overline{N}$ is small enough.

(3) $g(s, t, 0) = f(s, t)$ for all $(s, t) \in \lambda \times I$;

(4) $g(s, 0, u) = f(s, 0)$, and $g(s, 1, u) = f(s, 1)$ for all $s \in \lambda$.

These conditions define g on all of $\lambda \times I \times I$ except the part where $s' < s < 1, 0 < t < 1$, and $u > 0$. And it is now a standard operation to extend g to this set, noting that the extension will carry this set into $K - \overline{N}$.

Now g defines a homotopy of f into a new mapping $f' : \lambda \times I \to K$ which agrees with f on all points of $\lambda \times \{0\}$ and $\lambda \times \{1\}$, and carries $\{z_0\} \times I$ into z_0. Also all points mapped into $\bar{N}$ by f are left fixed throughout the deformation. It follows at once from Theorem 5 that this homotopy can be lifted into $V(K)$. (To apply Theorem 5, it is understood that $\lambda \times I$ is first identified with a set on S which plays the part of K in that theorem.) And so there is a mapping $F' : V(\lambda) \times I \to V(K)$ agreeing with F_0 and F_1 on $V(\lambda) \times \{0\}$ and $V(\lambda) \times \{1\}$, respectively, and carrying $V(z_0) \times I$ into $V(z_0)$.

But the point set union of λ and $\bar{N}_1$ is a deformation retract of K, from which it follows that F' can be replaced by a mapping F'' with similar properties but carrying $V(\lambda) \times I$ into $V(\lambda \cup \bar{N}_1)$ (Theorem 5). The proof of the lemma is then completed by shrinking $V(\bar{N}_1)$ onto $V(z')$, using Theorem 12 and noting that it has been arranged that such a shrinkage carries $V(\lambda)$ into itself (see the beginning of the proof of Lemma a).

The following is a variant of Lemma b which will be needed at the end of this chapter:

LEMMA c. *Let α_0 be as in Lemma b, and let a mapping $F : E^r \times I \to V(K) - L$ be given with the following properties:*

(1) *The restrictions of F to $E^r \times \{0\}$ and $E^r \times \{1\}$ are mappings F_0 and F_1 respectively of (E^r, S^{r-1}) into $(V(\lambda), V_0)$.*

(2) *$F(S^{r-1} \times \{t\}) \subset V(z(t))$, where $z(t)$ is the point of parameter t on α_0.*

Then F_0 and F_1 are homotopic, regarded as mappings into $(V(\lambda), V_0)$.

PROOF. The proof is a modification of that of Lemma b. Take E^r as the set in $(r + 1)$-space defined by $\sum_{i=1}^{r+1} x_i^2 = 1$, $-1 \leqslant x_1 \leqslant 0$. Let π be the projection of $V(K) - L$ onto K defined by mapping each point of $V(z)$ on the point $z \in K$. Then the mapping $f = \pi \circ F$ is defined. $f(S^{r-1} \times \{t\}) = z(t)$. If N is a sufficiently small neighbourhood of z' on K there is a number x_1' such that f carries the points of $E^r \times I$ defined by $x_1 \geqslant x_1'$ into $K - N$. Now define g as in Lemma b, replacing λ by E^r, s by x_1 and s' by x_1'. g can be lifted into $V(K) - L$ using this time the ordinary covering homotopy theorem of fibre bundles, and the proof is completed as before by a retraction onto $V(\lambda)$.

PROOF OF THEOREM 38. Let α_1 be a path from z_0 to z_0' in $K - z'$. Lemma a implies the existence of a homomorphism $T_{\mu\lambda}^{\alpha_1} : H_r(V(\lambda), V(z_0)) \to H_r(V(\mu), V(z_0'))$ such that $\partial T_{\mu\lambda}^{\alpha_1} = T_{\alpha_1}' \partial$ (i.e. the diagram in the statement of Theorem 38 with α replaced by α_1 is commutative). Let α_2 now be a path from z_0' to z_0 such that $\alpha_1\alpha_2$ is homotopic to a constant in $K - z'$. Then Lemma b shows that $T_{\lambda\mu}^{\alpha_2} T_{\mu\lambda}^{\alpha_1}$ and $T_{\mu\lambda}^{\alpha_1} T_{\lambda\mu}^{\alpha_2}$ are the identity homomorphisms. The required result follows at once.

There are two special cases of the above theorem to be used in the subsequent working, namely where the homotopy class α of the path from z_0 to z_0' corresponds respectively to a clockwise or anticlockwise rotation of λ into μ. The isomorphisms of $H_r(V(\lambda), V(z_0))$ onto $H_r(V(\mu), V(z_0'))$ obtained corresponding to these two homotopy classes will be denoted by $T_{\mu\lambda}^c$ and $T_{\mu\lambda}^a$, respectively. These are the isomorphisms whose existence was asserted in Theorem 33.

COROLLARY. *It is not hard to see that, if λ, μ, ν are three arcs radiating from z', appearing in the anticlockwise order λ, μ, ν, λ, then the compatibility relation $T_{\nu\lambda}^a = T_{\nu\mu}^a T_{\mu\lambda}^a$ holds.*

2. A special representative for δ

Referring back to §3, Chapter V, it will be seen that the vanishing cycle δ was constructed as the sum of a chain ν on $V(z_0, w')$ and two relative cycles $\Delta_1^{(r-1)}$ and $\Delta_2^{(r-1)}$ on $V(z_0, \lambda_1)$ and $V(z_0, \lambda_2)$ modulo $V(z_0, w')$, where λ_1 and λ_2 are paths in the complex w-plane joining w' to $w_1(z_0)$, respectively $w_2(z_0)$. And then referring to §2, Chapter VI, it appears that the paths μ_1 and μ_2 joining $w_1(z_0)$ and $w_2(z_0)$ to ∞ in the w-plane can be obtained from λ_1 and λ_2 by a clockwise and an anti-clockwise rotation, respectively. Let $T_{\mu_1\lambda_1}^c : H_{r-1}(V(z_0, \lambda_1), V(z_0, w'))$ $\to H_{r-1}(V(z_0, \mu_1), P)$ be the clockwise isomorphism constructed as in the last section, and $T^a_{\mu_2\lambda_2}$ the similar isomorphism relative to λ_2 and μ_2.

Then writing i_1 and i_2 for the injection homomorphisms of $H_{r-1}(V(z_0, \mu_1), P)$ and $H_{r-1}(V(z_0, \mu_2), P)$ into $H_{r-1}(V(z_0), P)$, define $\bar{\Delta}_1 = i_1 T^c_{\mu_1\lambda_1}(\bar{\Delta}_1^{(r-1)})$ and $\bar{\Delta}_2 = i_2 T^a_{\mu_2\lambda_2}(\bar{\Delta}_2^{(r-1)})$ where $\bar{\Delta}_1^{(r-1)}$ and $\bar{\Delta}_2^{(r-1)}$ are the relative homology classes of $\Delta_1^{(r-1)}$ and $\Delta_2^{(r-1)}$ in $V(z_0, \lambda_1)$ and $V(z_0, \lambda_2)$ modulo $V(z_0, w')$. Finally define Δ_1 and Δ_2 to be representative relative cycles for $\bar{\Delta}_1$ and $\bar{\Delta}_2$ respectively, obtained in the obvious way from $\Delta_1^{(r-1)}$ and $\Delta_2^{(r-1)}$.

It is clear, then, that $\delta = \nu + \Delta_1^{(r-1)} + \Delta_2^{(r-1)}$ is homologous to $\Delta_1 + \Delta_2$, modulo P. That is to say $\Delta_1 + \Delta_2$ is a representative of the element δ of $H_{r-1}(V(z_0), P)$, or $\delta = \bar{\Delta}_1 + \bar{\Delta}_2$. This justifies the choice of Δ_1 and Δ_2 made in §2, Chapter VI.

3. Proof of Theorem 32

The object of this section is to compute $T(\bar{\Delta}_1)$, where T is the automorphism of $H_{r-1}(V_0, P)$ induced by a closed path, say the circumference of a circle, going once round z' in the anti-clockwise direction. This will be done by examining first T^α, the isomorphism of $H_{r-1}(V(z_1), P)$ onto $H_{r-1}(V(z_2), P)$ induced by an open path α on the z-plane, going from z_1 to another ordinary point z_2. Theorem 5 ensures the existence of T^α (or alternatively an argument similar to that at the beginning of Chapter VI), and also that T^α depends only on the homotopy class of α in the z-plane with all special points removed, and with respect to the fixed end points z_1 and z_2.

The idea is eventually to take α as an arc on the circumference γ of a circle with centre z', and then, by dividing γ into a sequence of sufficiently small arcs, to calculate $T(\Delta_1)$ step by step, the point being that T^α is very easy to deal with for a sufficiently short arc α.

LEMMA. Let α be the arc on γ joining $z_1 = z(\theta_1)$ and $z_2 = z(\theta_2)$, in the notation of §2, Chapter VI. Let $\bar{\Delta}(\theta)$ be the image of a generator of $H_{r-1}(V(z(\theta)), \mu(\theta)), P)$ still in the notation of Chapter VI, under the injection into $H_{r-1}(V(z(\theta)), P)$. Then if θ_2 is near enough to θ_1, $T^\alpha(\bar{\Delta}(\theta_1)) = \pm\bar{\Delta}(\theta_2)$.

PROOF. In the complex w-plane let U be a neighbourhood of the path $\mu(\theta_1)$ such that $V(z(\theta_2), \mu(\theta_2))$ is a deformation retract of $V(z(\theta_2), U)$. Such a U certainly exists if θ_2 is sufficiently near to θ_1, at least if $\mu(\theta)$ is always piecewise analytic, and this can be assumed to be so. Now, by Theorem 19, $\bar{\Delta}(\theta_1)$ is the image of a generator of $H_{r-1}(E^{r-1}, S^{r-2})$ under the homomorphism induced by a continuous mapping $f_1 : (E^{r-1}, S^{r-2}) \to (V(z(\theta_1)), P)$, the image of f_1 being contained in $V(z(\theta_1), \mu(\theta_1))$. The construction of the homomorphism T^α involves the construction of a mapping $g : (V(z_1) \times I, P \times I) \to (V, P)$, which, restricted to $V(z_1) \times \{0\}$, coincides with the inclusion mapping $(V(z_1), P) \to (V, P)$, and which carries $V(z_1) \times \{1\}$ into $V(z_2)$. Write g' for the restriction of g to the set $V(z_1) \times \{1\}$. Then a simple argument from the compactness of E^{r-1} shows that, if θ_2 is sufficiently near to θ_1, the image of $g' f_1 = f_2$ will be entirely contained in $V(z(\theta_2), U)$. It follows at once from this that $T^\alpha(\bar{\Delta}(\theta_1))$ can be represented by a relative cycle of $V(z_2)$ modulo P which is in fact a chain on $V(z_2, U)$. Since the last-mentioned set can be retracted on $V(z(\theta_2), \mu(\theta_2))$, it follows from Theorem 12 (the retraction of U on $\mu(\theta_2)$ can be assumed to satisfy the necessary condition) that $T^\alpha(\bar{\Delta}(\theta_1))$ has a representative which is a relative cycle on $V(z(\theta_2), \mu(\theta_2))$ modulo P. Applying Theorem 19, it follows that $T^\alpha(\bar{\Delta}(\theta_1)) = c\bar{\Delta}(\theta_2)$ for some integer c. It still has to be checked that $c = \pm 1$.

Let α' be the path α taken in the opposite direction. Then, of course $\alpha\alpha'$ is homotopic to a constant on the circle γ. Let $T^\alpha : H_{r-1}(V(z_2), P) \to H_{r-1}(V(z_1), P)$ be constructed corresponding to α', as T^α corresponds to α. The composition of T^α and $T^{\alpha'}$, which is the identity isomorphism of $H_{r-1}(V(z_1), P)$ on itself, involves the construction of a mapping $h : V(z_1) \times I \to V$ such that h, restricted to $V(z_1) \times \{0\}$ is the identity, and $h(V(z_1) \times \{\frac{1}{2}\}) \subset V(z_2), h(V(z_1) \times \{1\}) \subset V(z_1)$. If h' is the restriction of h to $V(z_1) \times \{1\}$, then h' is homotopic to the identity, h' being here considered as a mapping of $V(z_1)$ into itself; that is to say, it depends continuously on θ_2. It follows at once that, if θ_2 is taken small enough, the images of $g' f_1$

(g' being the same as the restriction of h to $V(z_1) \times \{\frac{1}{2}\}$) and $h'_{\circ}f_1$ will be contained in $V(z_2, U)$ and $V(z_1, U)$, respectively. The above argument may then be repeated for $T^{\alpha'}$, the inverse of T^{α}, to show that $T^{\alpha'}(\bar{\Delta}(\theta_2)) = c'\bar{\Delta}(\theta_1)$, for some integer c'. Since $k\bar{\Delta}(\theta_1) \neq 0$ for any integer k (cf. Theorem 19) it follows from these results that $cc' = 1$, and so $c = \pm 1$, as required.

4. Proof of Theorem 34

As already indicated in Chapter VI the proof of this theorem will be carried out by constructing special models for representatives of $\bar{\Delta}$ and $T^a_{\mu\lambda}(\bar{\Delta})$. The construction will be carried out with the aid of the following preliminary considerations on hypersurfaces.

Let W_r be an algebraic (but not necessarily non-singular) hypersurface in affine $(z_1, z_2, \ldots, z_{r+1})$-space A_{r+1}, and let (ζ) be a generic point of W_r. Make a "parallel projection" (that is, from a point at infinity) along any direction in the tangent hyperplane to W_r at (ζ) onto a subspace A_r. Let W_{r-1} denote the branch locus in A_r corresponding to this projection; that is to say, $(z') \in W_{r-1}$ if and only if two or more points of W_r projecting on (z') are coincident. In particular, if (ζ) projects on (ζ'), then for any (z') in $A_r - W_{r-1}$ near (ζ'), there are just two points of W_r near (ζ) projecting on (z'). Also it is not hard to see that (ζ') is a generic point of W_{r-1}. And so a similar projection of W_{r-1} onto a subspace A_{r-1} of A_r may be made, this time along a direction parallel to the tangent hyperplane to W_{r-1} at (ζ') in A_r. The branch locus in A_{r-1} will be called W_{r-2}. And so on step by step until a curve W_1 is reached.

Now the condition that, in the first projection mentioned above, more than two points near (ζ) should project on a point near (ζ') is algebraic in the coordinates of (ζ), a similar statement holding for each subsequent projection. It follows at once that a point (ζ), no longer generic, can be taken as origin 0 of coordinates in A_{r+1} and the coordinates $(z_1, z_2, \ldots, z_{r+1})$ can be chosen so that the following condition holds:

(A) *For each $i = 1, 2, \ldots, r$, W_i has, in a sufficiently small neighbourhood of 0, the equation $z_{i+1}^2 + a_i z_{i+1} + b_i = 0$ in the space A_{i+1}, where a_i and b_i are analytic functions around 0 in the variables $z_1, z_2, \ldots, z_i$. Also a_i and b_i vanish at 0, and the only linear term in the expansion of b_i in powers of $z_1, z_2, \ldots, z_i$ is a non-zero term $c_i z_1$.*

Remembering that a generic hyperplane pencil contains at most a finite number of tangent hyperplanes to W_r' (using here the dual W_r' of W_r as in Chapter I; the possible existence of singularities makes no difference to this argument) each of which has a generic point of W_r as point of contact, it is not hard to see that a pencil can be selected containing at most a finite number of tangent hyperplanes of W_r such that, around each point of contact, coordinates can be chosen so that (A) holds. This is the context in which the results about to be described will eventually be used. In the meantime, let the origin 0 and the coordinates $(Z_1, z_2, \ldots, z_{r+1})$ be such that (A) holds.

A real analytic mapping of the solid r-sphere E^r into W_r is now to be constructed, carrying S^{r-1}, the boundary of E^r, into the section of W_r by the hyperplane $z_1 = c$, where c is a sufficiently small complex number. This mapping will actually be a homeomorphism into, and will map the centre of E^r on 0, and in addition will depend continuously on c, which will be allowed to vary on a certain arc on the z_1-plane. The mapping in question will be constructed inductively, starting off with the curve W_1. But first some notational conventions must be introduced.

The arc along which c is to vary will be an arc of a small circle about the origin in the z_1 plane, of radius ρ, say. It will be assumed that the arc in question goes in the anticlockwise direction from $c_0 = \rho e^{i\theta_0}$ to $c_1 = \rho e^{i\theta_1}$. Any point on this arc will be written as $c(t) = \rho e^{i\theta(t)}$, where $\theta(t) = (1 - t)\theta_0 + t\theta_1$. Also the following notations will be used:

$$E^i = \text{the set } \sum_{j=1}^{i+1} x_j^2 = 1, \ x_1 \leqslant 0 \text{ in real } (i + 1)\text{-space};$$

S^{i-1} = the set $\sum\limits_{j=1}^{i+1} x_{j|}^2 = 1$, $x_1 = 0$ in real $(i + 1)$-space;

E^{i-1} and S^{i-2} are the subsets of E^i and S^{i-1}, respectively, with $x_{i+1} = 0$;

H^{i+1} = the set $\sum\limits_{j=1}^{i+1} x_j^2 \leqslant 1$, $x_1 \leqslant 0$ in $(i + 1)$-space;

D^i = the subset of H^{i+1} for which $x_1 = 0$.

Consider now the curve W_1 in A_2 with the equation $z_2^2 + a_1 z_2 + b_1 = 0$ around the origin. The function $a_1^2 - 4b_1$ is zero at 0, and only at 0 in a sufficiently small neighbourhood of 0, and $db_1/dz_1 \neq 0$ at 0. Hence $a_1^2 - 4b_1 = z_1\phi_1$, where ϕ_1 is a function not zero in a neighbourhood of the origin. Define $f_1(x_1, x_2, t)$ for $(x_1, x_2) \in H^2$ and $0 \leqslant t \leqslant 1$ by $f_1(x_1, x_2, t)$ = the point (z_1, z_2) in A_2 where $z_1 = \rho(1 - x_1^2)e^{i\theta(t)}$, $z_2 = \frac{1}{2}(-a_1(z_1) + \sqrt{\rho}x_2 e^{\frac{1}{2}i\theta(t)}\sqrt{\phi_1(z_1)})$. z_1 is a complex valued real analytic function of x_1 and t, and z_2 of x_1, x_2, t (since ϕ_1 is not zero near $z_1 = 0$). D^1 (given by $x_1 = 0$) is mapped into $z_1 = \rho e^{i\theta(t)} = c(t)$. And if $(x_1, x_2) \in E^1$, $x_2 = \pm\sqrt{1 - x_1^2}$, and so $z_2 = \frac{1}{2}(-a_1(z_1) \pm \sqrt{z_1\phi_1(z_1)}) = \frac{1}{2}(-a_1 \pm \sqrt{a_1^2 - 4b_1})$. Hence E^1 is mapped into W_1. Clearly the point $(-1, 0)$ is mapped on $(0, 0)$. Finally, for any fixed t, f_1 is a homeomorphism on H^2, and only the points of E^1 are mapped into W_1.

The mapping f_1 is thus fully defined on $H^2 \times I$. Assume now that an analytic mapping $f_{i-1} . H^i \times I \to A_i$ has been constructed with the following properties:

(1) $f_{i-1}(D^{i-1} \times \{t\}) \subset$ the set $z_1 = c(t)$;

(2) $f_{i-1}(E^{i-1} \times I) \subset W_{i-1}$, and only $E^{i-1} \times I$ is mapped into W_{i-1};

(3) for fixed t, f_{i-1} is an analytic homeomorphism, carrying $(-1, 0, 0, \ldots, 0)$ into the origin;

(4) if $f_{i-1}(x_1, x_2, \ldots, x_i, t) = (z_1, z_2, \ldots, z_i)$ then $z_1 = \rho(1 - x_1^2)e^{i\theta(t)}$.

f_1 has been constructed with these properties; it will now be shown that the conditions stated enable a mapping f_i to be defined with similar properties.

By condition (2) on f_{i-1}, $a_i^2 - 4b_i$, when expressed by means of f_{i-1} in terms of x_1, x_2, ..., x_i, t, vanishes only on the set $\sum_{j=1}^{i} x_j^2 = 1$, and therefore contains $1 - \sum_1^i x_j^2$ as a factor, the other factor being also real analytic in x_1, x_2, ..., x_i, t. Write $x_1 + 1 = \xi$. Then $1 - \sum_1^i x_j^2 = 2\xi - \xi^2 - \sum_2^i x_j^2$.

The only linear term in $a_i^2 - 4b_i$, when expanded in a power series around the origin, is $c_i z_1$. That is to say $a_i^2 - 4b_i = c_i z_1 +$ higher powers of the z_j. By condition (4) above, when the z_j are expressed in terms of x_1, x_2, ..., x_i, t by means of f_{i-1}, $z_1 = \rho \xi(2 - \xi)e^{i\theta(t)} = 2\rho e^{i\theta(t)}\xi +$ term in ξ^2, and near $(-1, 0, 0, \ldots, 0)$ the other z_j are all power series with zero constant terms in ξ, x_2, x_3, ..., x_i. Hence $a_i^2 - 4b_i = 2c_i \rho e^{i\theta(t)}\xi +$ higher powers of ξ, x_2, x_3, ..., x_i. It follows that $a_i^2 - 4b_i$ contains the factor $1 - \sum_1^i x_j^2 = 2\xi - \xi^2 - \sum_2^i x_j^2$ exactly once. That is to say

$$a_i^2 - 4b_i = (1 - \sum_2^i x_j^2)\phi_i, \tag{1}$$

where $\phi_i = c_i \rho e^{i\theta(t)} +$ higher powers of ξ, x_2, x_3, ..., x_i, and $\phi_i \neq 0$ on H^i.

Now for $(x_1, x_2, \ldots, x_{i+1}) \in H^{i+1}$ and $0 \leqslant t \leqslant 1$, define $f_i(x_1, x_2, \ldots, x_{i+1}, t) = (z_1, z_2, \ldots, z_{i+1})$ by:

$$(z_1, z_2, \ldots, z_i) = f_{i-1}(x_1, x_2, \ldots, x_i, t),$$
$$z_{i+1} = \tfrac{1}{2}(-a_i + x_{i+1}\sqrt{\phi_i}). \tag{2}$$

$\phi_i \neq 0$ on H^i, and so $\sqrt{\phi_i}$ is real analytic on H^i. Hence f_i is a real analytic mapping. z_1 is given by f_{i-1} as $\rho(1 - x_1^2)e^{i\theta(t)}$; and so $f_i(D^i \times \{t\}) \subset$ the set $z_1 = c(t)$. If $(x_1, x_2, \ldots, x_{i+1}) \in E^i$, then $x_{i+1} = \pm(1 - \sum_1^i x_j^2)^{\frac{1}{2}}$, and (2) becomes the formula for solving the quadratic equation $z_{i+1}^2 + a_i z_{i+1} + b_i = 0$. That is to say, $f_i(E^i \times I) \subset W_i$. The converse, that $\overset{-1}{f_i}(W_i) = E^i \times I$, is easy to check, as is also the fact that f_i is a homeomorphism for any fixed t. Also $f_i(-1, 0, 0, \ldots, 0, t) = (0, 0, \ldots, 0)$ follows at once from the definition.

The mapping f_r, now simply to be called f, which has just been constructed is the essential tool in the intersection number calculation about to be carried out. The idea is to project the r-dimensional variety V, which is embedded in projective n-space, into an $(r + 1)$-dimensional space A_{r+1}, V projecting thus onto a hypersurface W_r of that space. This projection π can be made locally homeomorphic around the singular point C' of the singular section $V(z')$, carrying this point into the origin of suitably chosen affine coordinates in A_{r+1}, and it can be assumed that the pencil Π of hyperplanes in projective n-space projects into the pencil in A_{r+1} with the equations $z_1 = $ constant. It must also be assumed for this purpose that Π has been chosen so that the condition (**A**) is satisfied by W_r at the origin in A_{r+1}. This simply means adding yet another to the list of algebraic conditions mentioned in §1, Chapter III, which Π must not satisfy if it is to be sufficiently general for the proofs of Lefschetz's theorems. (cf. remark at end of §1, Chapter III).

Write g_0, g_1 for f restricted to $E^r \times \{0\}$, $E^r \times \{1\}$, respectively and let Δ_0 be a relative cycle of E^r modulo S^{r-1} representing a generator of $H_r(E^r, S^{r-1})$. Δ_0 can, in fact, be taken as a singular simplex or singular cell on E^r. Then $g_0(\Delta_0)$ and $g_1(\Delta_0)$ are singular cells on W_r, and it will turn out quite easy to calculate their intersection number. On the other hand, it will appear that they are projections, under π, of representatives of a generator $\bar{\Delta}$ of $H_r(V(\lambda), V_0)$ and of $T^\alpha(\bar{\Delta})$, respectively, where $V_0 = V(z_0)$ projects under π into the section of W_r by $z_1 = c_0$. The homeomorphic nature of π around C' will then give Theorem 34 at once.

THEOREM 39. *The intersection number* $(g_0(\Delta_0) . g_0(\Delta_1))$ *is* 1.

PROOF. The convention of orientation of a complex analytic manifold will first be stated. If $\zeta_1, \zeta_2, \zeta_3, \ldots, \zeta_r$, are local coordinates on such a manifold and $\zeta_j = \xi_j + i\eta_j$, then the standard orientation of the manifold is to be that corresponding to the order $\xi_1, \xi_2, \xi_3, \ldots, \xi_r, \eta_1, \ldots, \eta_r$ of real coordinates.

Then, in order to prove the theorem it is sufficient to show that the r tangent vectors on E at $(-1, 0, 0, \ldots, 0)$ parallel to the x_2, x_3, ..., x_{r+1} coordinate directions are carried by g_0 into vectors u_1, u_2, ..., u_r and by g_1 into vectors v_1, v_2, ..., v_r such that the vectors u_1, u_2, ..., u_r, v_1, ..., v_r, in that order, define the standard orientation of the tangent hyperplane to W_r at the origin. (For this to be true it may be necessary to restrict the size of the rotation from θ_0 to θ_1, or the simplex having u_1, u_2, ..., u_r, v_1, ..., v_r as edges will turn outside in.)

The theorem is true for $r = 1$, for the vectors u_1, v_1 in this case are given by joining the origin in the z_1-plane to the values of dz_2/dx_2 at $(-1,\ 0)$ for $t = 0$ and $t = 1$, respectively, the derivative being calculated from the formula $z_2 = \frac{1}{2}(-a_1(z_1) + \sqrt{\rho}x_2 e^{\frac{1}{2}i\theta(t)}\sqrt{\phi_1})$; it is clear that here the only restriction which must be made is the natural one $\theta_1 - \theta_0 < 2\pi$. Suppose, then, that it is true for r replaced by $r - 1$. That is to say, suppose that f_{r-1}, restricted to $t = 0$ and $t = 1$, carries the tangent vectors to E^{r-1} at $(-1, 0, 0, ..., 0)$ in the x_2, x_3, ..., x_r directions into two sets of vectors u_1, u_2, ..., u_{r-1}, v_1, ..., v_{r-1} such that the u_i and v_i, in that order, define the standard orientation on the tangent linear variety to W_{r-1} at the origin. There is a subvariety W'_{r-1} of W_r, transversal to the z_{r+1}-axis, projecting on W_{r-1} under the projection of W_r on A_r (given in fact by equation (2) with $i = r$ and with $x_{r+1} = 0$). The u_i and v_i lift into vectors u'_1, u'_2, ..., u'_{r-1}, v'_1, ..., v'_{r-1} spanning the tangent linear variety of W'_{r-1} at the origin, with the standard orientation. The directions of the image of the tangent to E^r at $(-1, 0, 0, ..., 0)$ in the x_{r+1} direction under g_0 and g_1 are given by the joins, in the z_{r+1}-plane, of the origin to the values of $\partial z_{r+1}/\partial x_{r+1}$ at $(-1, 0, ..., 0)$ for $t = 0$ and for $t = 1$. By (2), $\partial z_{r+1}/\partial x_{r+1} = \frac{1}{2}\sqrt{\phi_r} = \frac{1}{2}\sqrt{c_r\rho}\ e^{\frac{1}{2}i\theta(t)} +$ terms in ξ, x_2, ..., x_r. Setting $t = 0$ and $t = 1$, it follows at once that the two vectors u_r and v_r so obtained are such that v_r lies anticlockwise from u_r in the z_{r+1}-plane. Hence u_1, u_2, ..., u_r, v_1, v_2, ..., v_r define the standard orientation of the tangent linear variety to W_r at the origin, as was to be proved.

THEOREM 40. *Let π be the projection of V into the $(r + 1)$-space A_{r+1}, π being an analytic homeomorphism around the point C'. Let $\pi(V) = W_r$, $\pi(C') = 0$. Let coordinates in A_{r+1} be as described above in condition (A), and let the image of Π under π be the pencil with the equations $z_1 = constant$. Write $h_0 = \overset{1-}{\pi_\circ} g_0$, $h_1 = \overset{-1}{\pi_\circ} g_1$ and $h = \overset{-1}{\pi_\circ} f$, in the notations already introduced. Let $\bar{\Delta}_0$ be a generator of $H_r(E^r, S^{r-1})$ and let i and j be the inclusions $(V(\lambda), V_0) \to (V, V_0)$ and $(V(\mu), V(z_0')) \to (V, V(z_0'))$, in the notation of §2, Chapter VI. Then a generator $\bar{\Delta}$ of $H_r(V(\lambda), V_0)$ can be chosen so that $h_{0*}(\bar{\Delta}_0) = ci_*\bar{\Delta}$ and $h_{1*}(\bar{\Delta}_0) = cj_* T^a_{\mu\lambda}(\bar{\Delta})$ for some integer c.*

PROOF. $\bar{\Delta}$ and $T^a_{\mu\lambda}(\bar{\Delta})$ are generators of $H_r(V(\lambda), V(z_0))$ and $H_r(V(\mu), V(z_0'))$, respectively. Also the images of h_0 and h_1 can be made arbitrarily small. Theorem 19 implies that $h_{0*}(\bar{\Delta}_0) = ci_*\bar{\Delta}$ and $h_{1*}(\bar{\Delta}_0) = c'j_* T^a_{\mu\lambda}(\bar{\Delta})$ for integers c and c'. It must therefore be shown that $c = c'$.

Since a suitable neighbourhood of $V(z')$ can be retracted onto $V(\lambda)$, using Theorem 12, there is a mapping h_0': $(E^r, S^{r-1}) \to (V, V_0)$ homotopic to h_0 such that $h_0'(E^r) \subset V(\lambda)$. Similarly there is a mapping h_1' homotopic to h_1 and having its image in $V(\mu)$. Hence $h_{0*}'(\bar{\Delta}_0) = ci_*\bar{\Delta}$ and $h_{1*}'(\bar{\Delta}_0) = c'j_* T^a_{\mu\lambda}(\bar{\Delta})$. Now, h_0' and h_1' are homotopic, the set S^{r-1} being carried at stage t of the homotopy into $V(z(t))$. On the other hand the construction of Lemma a, §1, induces a homotopy of h_0' and a mapping $h_1'': (E^r, S^{r-1}) \to (V, V(z_0'))$ with its image in $V(\mu)$ and such that $h_{1*}''(\bar{\Delta}) = cj_* T^a_{\mu\lambda}(\bar{\Delta})$. To complete the proof it must be shown that h_1' and h_1'', as mappings into $(V(\mu), V(z_0'))$ are homotopic. That this is so follows at once from Lemma c of §1.

The proof of Theorem 34 can now be carried out. For, by Theorem 39, along with the fact that π is locally homeomorphic around C', $(h_0(\Delta_0) . h_1(\Delta_0)) = 1$, and so, by Theorem 40, $c^2(\Delta . T'(^a_{\mu\lambda}\Delta)) = 1$. c is an integer and so $c^2 = 1$, whence $(\Delta . T^a_{\mu\lambda}(\Delta)) = 1$, as required.

CHAPTER VIII

INVARIANT CYCLES AND RELATIVE CYCLES

1. Summary of results assumed

As already explained in Chapter VI, the fundamental group of the complex sphere S with the special points $z_1, \ldots, z_k$ removed acts as a group G of automorphisms on $H_q(V_0, P)$. For $q = r - 1$ the form of the basic elements of this automorphism group has been established in Chapters VI and VII. The term "invariant element of $H_q(V_0, P)$" will now be used to denote an element which is invariant under G. If $\bar{\alpha} \in H_q(V_0, P)$ is an invariant element and α a relative cycle of V_0 modulo P representing $\bar{\alpha}$, then α will be called an invariant relative cycle.

Theorem 30 shows that every element of $H_q(V_0, P)$ is invariant for $q \leqslant r - 2$, and so interesting results will only be obtained for $q = r - 1$. The first result to be obtained in this chapter is essentially that $H_{r-1}(V_0, P)$, with coefficients in the rational numbers instead of the integers, is the direct sum of its subgroup of invariant elements and of the kernel of the injection $H_{r-1}(V_0, P) \to H_{r-1}(V, P)$. Being a result on homology with rational coefficients this lends itself readily to a treatment involving the de Rham cohomology on V. The following results will be used:

(a) A Kähler structure may be given to V, induced by a Kähler structure of the ambient projective space in such a way that, if Ω is the fundamental quadratic exterior form of the Kähler structure, Ω is homologous in the de Rham sense to the image under the injection map $H_{2r-2}(V_0) \to H_{2r-2}(V)$ of a generator of the first of these groups.

(b) Let ϕ be a differential form on V and write $L\phi = \Omega \wedge \phi$ and let Λ be the dual operator to L (Weil [12]). Then if ϕ is of degree $>r$, $\Lambda\phi = 0$ implies $\phi = 0$, and dually if ϕ is of degree $<r$, $L\phi = 0$ implies $\phi = 0$.

(c) Every form of degree $<r$ can be written as $\Lambda\phi$, and dually, every form of degree $>r$ can be written as $L\phi$.

(d) It follows from (b) and (c) that L effects a homomorphism L^* of $H^q(V)$ into $H^{q+2}(V)$, where the upper indices denote cohomology groups, which is onto for $q > r - 2$ and isomorphic for $q < r$.

(e) Every form ϕ of degree $\leqslant r$ can be written uniquely as $\phi_0 + L\phi_1 + L^2\phi_2 + \ldots$, where $\Lambda\phi_i = 0$ for each i. Using (b) and (c) this unique decomposition can be extended to forms of degree $r + 1$.

(f) The operator L and the induced homomorphism $L^* : H^q(V) \to H^{q+2}(V)$ give rise at once to a homomorphism in homology. For, by Poincaré duality on the manifold V there are isomorphisms $\theta_q : H^q(V) \cong H_{2r-q}(V)$ for each q. Then writing $L_* = \theta_{q+2}L^*\theta_q^{-1}$ one obtains a homomorphism $L_* : H_q(V) \to H_{q-2}(V)$ for each q, and by (d) above L_* is onto for $q < r + 2$ and is isomorphic for $q > r$.

The standard interpretation of L_* is as an intersection of a representative of an element of $H_q(V)$ with a fundamental cycle of V_0. This interpretation will be discussed in greater detail later in the chapter. In the meantime the following lemma will be stated; it is essentially part of Hodge's classification of the cycles on an algebraic variety (cf. Hodge [6], [7]), and follows at once from the definition of L_* and the above stated properties of the operator L:

LEMMA. *An element of $H_q(V)$ for $q \geqslant r$ is in the image of L_* if and only if it is in the image of the injection $H_q(V_0) \to H_q(V)$. An element of $H_{r-1}(V)$ is in the image of L_*^2 if and only if it is in the image of the injection $H_{r-1}(P) \to H_{r-1}(V)$.*

2. The intersection and locus operators

As in some of the earlier parts of this monograph, it is convenient at this stage to sketch some of the results required geometrically, in order not to delay too much the main theorems. The details of these sketched proofs will then be completed in §5. In the first place some intersection operators, of which L_* is one, will be described (cf. §5 for further details).

Let V_0 and V_1 be two non-singular hyperplane sections of V belonging to the pencil Π. Then if $\bar{\alpha} \in H_q(V)$, $\bar{\alpha}$ has a representative cycle α which is intersected by V_1 in a cycle β. The homology class of β in V is $L_* \bar{\alpha}$.

Secondly if $\bar{\alpha} \in H_q(V, V_0)$, $\bar{\alpha}$ has a representative relative cycle which intersects V_1 in a relative cycle β of V_1 modulo P. The image of the relative homology class of β in V_1 modulo P under a suitable isomorphism of $H_{q-2}(V_1, P)$ onto $H_{q-2}(V_0, P)$ will be denoted by $L_0 \bar{\alpha}$. The relative homology class of β in V modulo P will be denoted by $L_1 \bar{\alpha}$.

Finally if $\bar{\alpha} \in H_{q-1}(V_0)$, there is a representative cycle intersecting V_1, that is to say intersecting P, in a cycle β. The homology class of β in P will be denoted by $L_2 \bar{\alpha}$.

The operators L_*, L_0, L_1, L_2 are all homomorphisms between the appropriate homology groups, L_* being the homomorphism introduced in §1, and L_*, L_1, L_2 fit together to form the following commutative diagram, in which the two rows are parts of the homology sequences of the pairs (V, V_0) and (V, P).

$$H_q(V) \to H_q(V, V_0) \to H_{q-1}(V_0) \to H_{q-1}(V)$$
$$\downarrow L_* \qquad \downarrow L_1 \qquad \qquad \downarrow L_2 \qquad \qquad \downarrow$$
$$H_{q-2}(V) \to H_{q-2}(V, P) \leftarrow H_{q-3}(P) \leftarrow H_{q-3}(V)$$

The operator L_0 starts from relative cycles of V modulo V_0 and yields relative cycles of V_0 modulo P. A partial inverse to this operation will now be constructed, namely, an operation which starts from relative cycles of V_0 modulo P and, under suitable conditions, gives relative cycles of V modulo V_0, with the dimension increased by two. As usual let $z_1, z_2, \ldots, z_k$ be the special points on S, and $\lambda_1, \lambda_2, \ldots, \lambda_k$ a set of arcs from an ordinary point z_0 to the special points, z_0 being the only common point of any two of the λ_i. Let K_0 be the point-set union of the λ_i. Let α be a q-dimensional relative cycle of $V_0 = V(z_0)$ modulo P. The idea now is to shift z_0 into $S - K_0$ and then allow it to vary over the whole of this set. As the section $V(z)$, starting at V_0, varies in this way, it carries with it the relative cycle α, which thus traces out a locus of dimension $q + 2$. This locus is a relative cycle of V modulo $V(K_0)$. The operator whose definition is based on this geometrical idea is thus a homomorphism of $H_q(V_0, P)$ into $H_{q+2}(V, V(K_0))$; this homomorphism will be denoted by loc.

Now the locus of a relative cycle of V_0 modulo P, constructed as just described may not be a relative cycle modulo V_0; because, as z varies over the cut complex sphere $S - K_0$, α may, so to speak, tend to different limits as z approaches one of the cuts from different sides. It is, however, reasonable to hope that, if α represents an invariant element of $H_q(V_0, P)$, then the limits as the λ_i are approached from opposite sides can be made the same, and the resulting locus will have its boundary in V_0. That this conjecture is valid will be shown by proving the following theorem:

THEOREM 41. *For* $\bar{\alpha} \in H_{r-1}(V_0, P)$, *loc$\bar{\alpha}$ is in the image of the homomorphism* $\pi\colon H_{r+1}(V, V_0) \to H_{r+1}(V, V(K_0))$, *induced by the appropriate inclusion mapping, if and only if* $\bar{\alpha}$ *is invariant, in the sense introduced at the beginning of* §1.

Note that, in accordance with the remark on invariant elements made at the beginning of §1, attention is confined to dimension $r - 1$. The proof of this theorem will be given in §5.

The next step is to establish a connection between the homomorphisms L_0 and loc. It is not hard to conjecture that, if one starts from an invariant relative cycle α of V_0 modulo P, forms its locus and then intersects this locus by V_0, one gets the relative cycle α back again. That is to say, the composition L_0loc, applied to invariant elements, is the identity. This will not be proved in detail as it is not needed. What is more important for the present purpose is to examine the composition locL_0. If α is a relative $(r + 1)$-cycle of V modulo V_0, the operation locL_0 means geometrically intersecting α with V_0 and then constructing the locus of this intersection as z varies over $S - K_0$. Now if the intersection of α with V_0 turns out to be invariant, then its locus can be represented as a relative cycle of V modulo V_0 (Theorem 41), and it will turn out that this relative cycle is homologous to the original α. That is to say it will be shown that the composition $\mathrm{loc}L_0$ coincides with the homomorphism π : $H_{r+1}(V,V_0) \to H_{r+1}(V,\ V(K))$ induced by inclusion.

The consequence of the relation $\mathrm{loc}L_0 = \pi$ which is wanted here is that the image of L_0 is in the invariant sub-group of $H_{r-1}(V_0,\ P)$. The opposite inclusion relation will also be obtained, and so the following result will be established:

THEOREM 42. *The image of* $L_0 : H_{r+1}(V,\ V_0) \to H_{r-1}(V_0,\ P)$ *consists of the invariant elements of* $H_{r-1}(V_0,\ P)$.

3. Direct decomposition for $H_{r-1}(V_0,\ P)$

On the basis of the results whose proofs were sketched in the last section, one of the main theorems of this chapter can be derived. The proof will be carried out with the aid of the following lemma:

LEMMA. *The homomorphism* $L_1 : H_{r+1}(V,\ V_0) \to H_{r-1}(V,\ P)$ *introduced in the last section (and for dimension* $r + 1$*) is an isomorphism.*

PROOF. Consider the following diagram:

$$H_{r+1}(V_0) \xrightarrow{i} H_{r+1}(V) \xrightarrow{j} H_{r+1}(V,\ V_0) \xrightarrow{\partial} H_r(V_0)$$
$$\downarrow{i'} \quad \downarrow{L_*} {\scriptstyle j'} \quad \downarrow{L_1} \quad {\scriptstyle \partial'} \downarrow{L_2} \quad h$$
$$H_{r-1}(P) \to H_{r-1}(V) \to H_{r-1}(V,\ P) \to H_{r-2}(P) \to H_{r-2}(V_0)$$

where L_*, L_1, L_2 are as in §2, ∂, ∂' are boundary homomorphisms and the other mappings are all induced by the appropriate inclusions. It is to be shown that the kernel of L_1 is zero. Let α be an element of this kernel; that is to say $L_1\alpha = 0$. Then $\partial'L\alpha = 0$ and so, by the commutativity of the diagram, $L_2\partial\alpha = 0$. Hence $hL_2\partial\alpha = 0$. Now hL_2 is a mapping constructed for V_0 in the same way as L_* is constructed for V, and so, for dimension r, it is an isomorphism (see (f) in §1). Thus $\partial\alpha = 0$ and so $\alpha = j\beta$ for some $\beta \in H_{r+1}(V)$. The equation $L_1 j\beta = L_1\alpha = 0$ becomes, by commutativity of the diagram, $j'L_*\beta = 0$. Then $L_*\beta$ is in the image of i' and so, by the lemma in §1, is in the image of L_*^2. That is to say $L_*\beta = L_*^2\gamma$ for some γ in $H_{r+3}(V)$. But (see (f) in §1) L_* is an isomorphism for dimension $r + 1$, and so $\beta = L_*\gamma$. Then, again by the lemma of §1, β is in the image of i, and so $\alpha = j\beta = 0$, as required.

THEOREM 43. $H_{r-1}(V_0, P)$ is the direct sum of the group of invariant elements and the kernel of the injection i: $H_{r-1}(V_0, P) \to H_{r-1}(V, P)$.

PROOF. Consider the diagram:

$$H_{r+1}(V, V_0) \overset{L_1}{\to} H_{r+1}(V, P)$$
$$L_0 \searrow \qquad \nearrow i$$
$$H_{r-1}(V_0, P)$$

By the definitions of L_0 and L_1 this diagram is commutative. Thus L_0 and iL_1 have as image some subgroup G of $H_{r-1}(V, P)$, and regarded as a map onto G, L_1 will have an inverse L_1^{-1} (by the above lemma). Hence $(L_1^{-1}i)L_0$ is the identity and so $H_{r-1}(V_0, P)$ is the direct sum of the image of L_0 and the kernel of $L_1^{-1}i$, which is the kernel of i. But the image of L_0 has been identified in Theorem 42 as the group of invariant elements of $H_{r-1}(V_0, P)$.

4. Direct decomposition of $H_{r-1}(V_0)$

The result of §3 is to give a direct decomposition of $H_{r-1}(V_0, P)$, the homology groups being with real or rational coefficients. A similar result will now be obtained for $H_{r-1}(V_0)$, and this will actually be Lefschetz's result (Lefschetz [9], Theorem I, p. 93). Returning to the notations of §1, Chapter VI, the fundamental group of K acts as a group of automorphisms on $H_q(X_0)$, where $X_0 = V_0$ is the fibre of the bundle X. If S'_α is the automorphism corresponding to the element α of $\pi_1(K)$, write $T'_\alpha = \psi_{0*}S'_\alpha\bar\psi_{0*}^{-1}$. Then the T'_α form a representation of $\pi_1(K)$ as a group of automorphisms on $H_q(V_0)$ for each q, just as the T_α of Chapter VI represented $\pi_1(K)$ as an automorphism group on $H_q(V_0, P)$.

An element of $H_q(V_0)$ invariant under the T'_α will simply be called an invariant element of $H_q(V_0)$. The analogue of Theorem 30 is practically trivial:

THEOREM 44. *The entire group $H_q(V_0)$ is invariant for $q \leqslant r - 2$.*

From now onwards attention will be fixed on the value $r - 1$ of q. Write $T'_i = T'_{\alpha_i}$, where the α_i are as in §1, Chapter VI, and let δ'_i denote the element of $H_{r-1}(V_0)$ represented by the vanishing cycle δ_i, while $\bar{\delta}_i$ denotes the element of $H_{r-1}(V_0, P)$ represented by the same cycle, for each $i = 1, 2, \ldots, k$.

LEMMA. *The homomorphism $H_{r-1}(V_0) \to H_{r-1}(V_0, P)$ induced by inclusion carries the kernel of the injection $H_{r-1}(V_0) \to H_{r-1}(V)$ isomorphically into that of the injection $H_{r-1}(V_0, P) \to H_{r-1}(V, P)$.*

PROOF. The two kernels mentioned are already known to consist of essentially the same elements, namely linear combinations of the "vanishing cycles." It must therefore be shown that if α is in the kernels of the mappings $H_{r-1}(V_0) \to H_{r-1}(V_0, P)$ and $H_{r-1}(V_0) \to H_{r-1}(V)$, induced by inclusions, then $\alpha = 0$. The proof is to be based on the following diagram:

$$
\begin{array}{ccccc}
H_{r+2}(V, V_0) \xrightarrow{\partial} & H_{r+1}(V_0) \xrightarrow{k} & H_{r+1}(V) & & \\
\downarrow L_1 & \downarrow L_2 & \downarrow L_* & & \\
H_r(V, P) \xrightarrow{\partial'} & H_{r-1}(P) \xrightarrow{k'} & H_{r-1}(V) \to & H_{r-1}(V, P) & \\
\uparrow i'' \quad \nearrow \partial'' & h \searrow & \uparrow i & \uparrow i' & \\
H_r(V_0, P) & & H_{r-1}(V_0) \xrightarrow{j} & H_{r-1}(V_0, P) &
\end{array}
$$

It is to be shown that j is an isomorphism between the kernels of i and i'. Clearly j maps the first of these kernels onto the second. Then let α be such that $i\alpha = j\alpha = 0$; it is to be shown that $\alpha = 0$. By the exactness of the homology sequence of (V_0, P), $j\alpha = 0$ implies that α is in the image of h. Now hL_2 corresponds to V_0 in the same way as L_* corresponds to V, and so the lemma at the end of §1 shows that α is in the image of hL_2. That is to say $\alpha = hL_2\beta$ for some $\beta \in H_{r+1}(V_0)$. Then $i\alpha = 0$ becomes $ihL_2\beta = 0$, in other words $k'L_2\beta = 0$, or $L_*k\beta = 0$, making use here of the commutativity of the above diagram. But L_* is an isomorphism for dimension

$r + 1$ (see (f), §1), and so $k\beta = 0$. Using the exactness of the top line of the diagram, it follows that $\beta = \partial\gamma$ for some $\gamma \in H_{r+2}(V, \ V_0)$. Hence $\alpha = hL_2\partial\gamma = h\partial'L_1\gamma$. But the image of L_1 is, by its definition, contained in that of i'', and so $\partial'L_1\gamma$ is in the image of $\partial'i'' = \partial''$. Thus α is in the image of $h\partial''$ which is zero by the exactness of the homology sequence of the pair (V_0, P).

The Poincaré formula for $H_{r-1}(V_0)$ can now be proved:

THEOREM 45. *For each* $\bar\alpha \in H_{r-1}(V_0)$, $T'_i(\bar\alpha) = \bar\alpha - (\alpha \cdot \delta_i)\delta'_i$, *the homology group being over integral coefficients.*

PROOF. Denote by π the projection map $H_{r-1}(V_0) \to H_{r-1}(V_0, P)$. Then $\pi\delta'_i = \delta_i$. A repetition of the argument of Theorem 31 yields at once that $T'_i(\bar\alpha) = \bar\alpha + c(\alpha \cdot \delta_i)\delta'_i$, where c is an integer independent of $\bar\alpha$. Now it is clear from the mode of construction of the T_i and T'_i that $\pi T'_i(\bar\alpha) = T_i(\pi\bar\alpha)$, and so $T_i(\pi\bar\alpha) = \pi\bar\alpha + c(\alpha \cdot \delta_i)\delta_i = \pi\bar\alpha - (\alpha \cdot \delta_i)\delta_i$, by Theorem 37. Now if δ_i is not a divisor of zero, that is if $n\delta_i \neq 0$ for all integers n, the last equation implies that $c(\alpha \cdot \delta_i) = -(\alpha \cdot \delta_i)$, and there will be at least one $\bar\alpha$ such that the intersection number is non-zero, whence $c = -1$ as required. On the other hand if $n\delta_1 = 0$ for some integer n, the above Lemma implies that δ'_i is a divisor of zero and so $(\alpha \cdot \delta_i) = 0$. The formula $T'_i(\bar\alpha) = \bar\alpha - (\alpha \cdot \delta_i)\delta'_i$, with the second term on the right vanishing, therefore still holds.

COROLLARY. $\bar\alpha$ *is invariant under all the* T'_i *if and only if* $\pi\bar\alpha$ *is invariant under all the* T_i, *the coefficients for the homology groups again being integers.*

The coefficients for the homology groups will again be assumed to be the rational or real numbers, as they have been throughout this chapter apart from the last theorem. The main result of this section is the following:

THEOREM 46. $H_{r-1}(V_0)$ *is the direct sum of the subgroup of elements invariant under the* T'_i *and the kernel of the injection* $H_{r-1}(V_0) \to H_{r-1}(V)$.

Let $\alpha \in H_{r-1}(V_0)$ and let π be as in Theorem 45. Then, by Theorem 43, $\pi\alpha = \alpha_1 + \alpha_0$ where α_1 is invariant under the T_i and α_0 is in the kernel of the injection $H_{r-1}(V_0, P) \to$

$H_{r-1}(V, P)$. But this kernel is generated by elements represented by the vanishing cycles, and so $\alpha_0 = \pi\alpha_0'$, for some $\alpha_0' \in H_{r-1}(V_0)$. Thus $\alpha_1 = \pi(\alpha - \alpha_0')$ is invariant under the T_i, and so, by the corollary of Theorem 45, $\alpha - \alpha_0' = \alpha_1'$ is invariant under the T_i'. And so $\alpha = \alpha_0' + \alpha_1'$, for α_1' invariant and α_0' in the kernel of $H_{r-1}(V_0) \to H_{r-1}(V)$. It must be shown that this expression is unique; that is to say, that $\alpha_0' + \alpha_1' = 0$ implies $\alpha_0' = 0$ and $\alpha_1' = 0$. But $\alpha_0' + \alpha_1' = 0$ implies that $\pi\alpha_0' + \pi\alpha_1' = 0$, and so, since the summation is direct in Theorem 43, $\pi\alpha_0' = 0$ and $\pi\alpha_1' = 0$. But by the lemma preceding Theorem 45, $\pi\alpha_0' = 0$ implies $\alpha_0' = 0$ and so also $\alpha_1' = 0$, as required.

Now, it is not hard to see from the definition of L_* sketched in §2 that it can be written as iL_{0*} where i is the injection $H_{q-2}(V_0) \to H_{q-2}(V)$ and L_{0*} is the homomorphism $H_q(V) \to H_{q-2}(V_0)$ represented by intersecting cycles of V with V_0 to obtain cycles of V_0. The following is then an immediate consequence of Theorem 46.

THEOREM 47. *The image in $H_{r-1}(V_0)$ of L_{0*} coincides with the group of invariant elements.*

PROOF. $iL_{0*} = L_*$ and L_* is an isomorphism onto for dimension r (see (f), §1). Thus $(\overset{-1}{L_*}i)L_{0*}$ is the identity, and so, by the usual argument applied to a homomorphism with a one-sided inverse, $H_{r-1}(V_0)$ is the direct sum of the image of L_{0*} and the kernel of $\overset{-1}{L_*}i$, that is, the kernel of i. Comparison with Theorem 46 then gives the result.

Finally, as a complement to Theorem 41, a result will be obtained on the locus of an invariant element of $H_{r-1}(V_0)$. In the following diagram:

$$H_{r+1}(V, V(K_0))$$

$$H_{r+1}(V, V_0) \xrightarrow{\ L_0\ } H_{r-1}(V_0, P)$$

$$H_{r+1}(V) \xrightarrow{\ L_{0*}\ } H_{r-1}(V_0)$$

π, π_1, π_2 are induced by inclusions. For the verification of commutativity, see §5.

THEOREM 48. *If* $\alpha \in H_{r-1}(V_1)$, α *is invariant if and only if* $loc\pi_2\alpha$ *is in the image of* $\pi\pi_1$.

For $\pi\pi_1 = loc\pi_2 L_{0*}$ and so if $loc\pi_2\alpha = \pi\pi_1\beta$, $\beta \in H_{r+1}(V)$ it follows that $loc\pi_2\alpha = loc\pi_2 L_{0*}\beta$, and so, since loc is an isomorphism (see §5), $\pi_2(\alpha - L_{0*}\beta) = 0$. Since $\alpha - L_{0*}\beta$ is in the kernel of π_2, the lemma of §1 implies $\alpha - L_{0*}\beta = L'_*\gamma$, where L'_* is related to V_0 as L_* to V. But commutativity holds in the diagram:

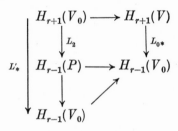

where the unmarked maps are induced by inclusions, and so $L'_*\gamma = L_{0*}\gamma'$, for $\gamma' \in H_{r+1}(V)$, and so α is in the image of L_{0*}, and so is invariant, by Theorem 47. Conversely if α is invariant, $\alpha = L_{0*}\beta$ for some $\beta \in H_{r+1}(V)$, and so $\pi\pi_1\beta = loc\pi_2 L_{0*}\beta = loc\pi_2\alpha$, as required.

5. Proofs of Theorems 41 and 42

In this section the details of the definitions and results of §2 will be filled in. The first step is to give the full geometrical definitions of the operators L_*, L_1, L_2, L_0. In order to do this, let V_0 and V_1 be two non-singular sections of V by hyperplanes of the pencil Π. Let B_1 be the normal bundle to V_1 in V, with respect to some Riemann metric on V, and let B_0 be the normal bundle of $V_0 \cap V_1$ in V_0 with respect to the induced metric. It is not hard to see that, if the radii of these bundles are small enough, the fibres of B_1 in a neighbourhood of $V_0 \cap V_1$ can be modified so that B_1 is refibred as a bundle B having the property that the fibres of B through points of $V_0 \cap V_1$ lie in V_0 and coincide with the corresponding fibres of B_0. Let B' and B_0' denote the boundaries of B and B_0, respectively. Thus, while B and B_0 are fibred by 2-cells, B' and B_0' are fibred by circles.

Since V_1 is an orientable submanifold of the orientable manifold V, the fibres of B can be consistently oriented, from which it follows that B and B' are trivial bundles and can be represented as products $V \times E^2$ and $V \times S^1$, where E^2 is a 2-cell and S^1 its circumference. Similarly writing $P = V_0 \cap V_1$ as usual, B_0 and B_0' can be represented as products $P \times E^2$ and $P \times S^1$, respectively. .

Consider now the diagram on page 108:

The vertical lines are all portions of the appropriate homology sequences. The mappings in the left-hand half of the diagram are induced by inclusion mappings, and so that part of the diagram is certainly commutative. In particular, the mappings between the second and third columns are excisions, and so may, in fact, be reversed. The isomorphisms marked in the middle of the diagram are obtained by identifying B, B_0, B', B_0' as products, as indicated above. The way in which B_0 and B_0' have been arranged to be the restrictions of B and B', corresponding to the restriction of the base from V_1 to P, ensures that commutativity holds between the third and fourth columns of the diagram. The mappings between the fourth and fifth columns are also isomorphisms, obtained by identifying $H_2(E^2, S^1)$ with the group of integers, at the same time making use of some homeomorphism of the pair (V_1, P) onto (V_0, P). The remaining mappings on the right are induced by inclusions. Commutativity in the right-hand half of the diagram is easily seen to hold.

The operators of §2 can now be defined:

L_* is the composition of all the mappings from left to right along the second row of the above diagram (remembering that the second mapping is an isomorphism onto and is to be reversed). It is a standard result, proved, say, by effecting a simplicial subdivision of V so that V_1 is a subcomplex, that this operator coincides with that obtained in §1 by way of differential forms and the de Rham theorems.

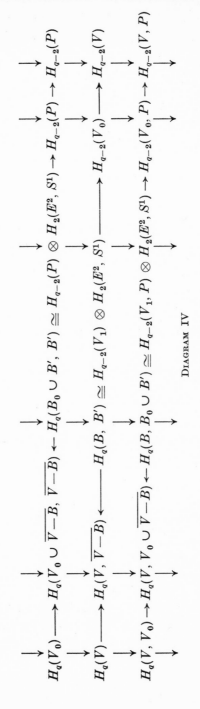

DIAGRAM IV

L_0 is the composition of all the mappings from left to right along the third row of the diagram, stopping at $H_{q-2}(V_0, P)$.

L_1 is similar to L_0 but goes right to the end of the third row of the diagram.

L_2 is the composition of all the mappings along the first row of the diagram from left to right.

It will be seen now that the diagram on p. 99 is simply a summary of the above diagram obtained by omitting everything except the first and last columns, and also writing these columns as rows. Thus the commutativity of the diagram of §2 is established, and also that of the other diagrams in §§2–4, is so far as they involve the operators L_*, etc.

The operator L_{0*} which appears in Theorems 47 and 48 is obtained by composing all the mappings of the second row of the above diagram, stopping this time at $H_{q-2}(V_0)$. The lower part of the diagram of Theorem 47 is thus again merely a summary of part of the above diagram, and so is commutative.

The operation loc will now be defined. K_0 is to be as described in §2. Let z_0' be a point of S not in K_0, and let K be a closed circular neighbourhood of z_0' not meeting K_0. Let K' be the circumference of K. It is not hard to see that there is a homotopy of the identity mapping of S on itself into a mapping which carries $\overline{S-K}$ into K_0, and moreover that the retraction of $\overline{S-K}$ on K_0 can be carried out along a family of curves with the properties listed in Chapter II, §1. It follows at once, using Theorems 5 and 12, that there is a homotopy of the identity mapping of V on itself into a mapping which carries $V(\overline{S-K})$ into $V(K_0)$.

The result just obtained implies that $H_q(V, V(K_0)) \cong H(V, V(\overline{S-K}))$ for all q. Next the excision result, Theorem 7, can be applied along with Theorem 5 to show that $H_q(V, V(\overline{S-K})) \cong H_q(V(K), V(K'))$ for all q. Then from the corollary to Theorem 10 it follows that $H_q(V(K), V(K')) \cong H_q(X(K), X(K') \cup X'(K))$, using here the notations introduced in Chapter I. But the bundle $X(K)$ can be identified with the product $V_1 \times K$ (writing $V(z_0') = V_1$) and the subset $X(K') \cup X'(K)$ with $(P \times K) \cup (V_1 \times K')$. And so

$$H_q(X(K), X(K') \cup X'(K)) \cong H_{q-2}(V_1, P) \otimes H_2(K, K')$$
$$\cong H_{q-2}(V_0, P)$$

the last isomorphism being obtained by identifying $H_2(K, K')$ with the group of integers and using some isomorphism of $H_{q-2}(V_1, P)$ onto $H_{q-2}(V_0, P)$ (for convenience this should be the same as the isomorphism already used in going from the fourth to the fifth column of Diagram IV. The composition of all these isomorphisms, taking the sequence in reverse, gives an isomorphism of $H_{q-2}(V_0, P)$ onto $H_q(V, V(K_0))$ which is to be denoted by loc. The fact that loc is an isomorphism should be noted; it is used for example in the proof of Theorem 48.

To obtain the connection, mentioned in §2, between loc and L_0, consider the diagram on page 111.

Here the mapping at the extreme right is the isomorphism referred to a moment ago. The mappings in the rectangle on the right are induced by the following commutative diagram:

$$
\begin{array}{ccc}
(B, \overline{B - V(K)}) & \leftarrow & (V(K), V(K')) \\
\uparrow & & \uparrow \psi \\
(B, B_0 \cup B') & \xleftarrow{\phi} & (X(K), X(K') \cup X'(K))
\end{array}
$$

where the mapping ψ is that introduced in Theorem 4, and ϕ is induced by noting that $B = E^2 \times V_1$ and $X(K) = K \times V_1$, and by identifying E^2 with K, while the remaining two mappings are inclusions. It follows that the rectangle on the right of Diagram (V) is commutative. The remaining mappings of Diagram (V) are all induced by inclusions, and so the whole diagram is commutative.

Comparison of the Diagrams (IV) and (V) shows that the composition of all the mappings along the bottom of (V) from left to right (reversing the excision isomorphism second on the left) is L_0. (It will be noted that the identification of B as a product, which was left unspecified in (IV) has now been made just so that (IV) and (V) will be compatible).

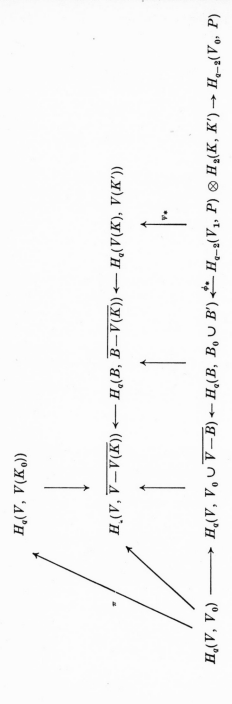

DIAGRAM V

Also, by comparing Diagram (V) with the definition of loc which precedes it, it is easy to see that loc is the composition of all the mappings along the upper right-hand edge of (V), zig-zagging from right to left, and reversing the arrows which point the wrong way, these being in any case isomorphisms.

Now the inclusion $H_q(V, V_0) \to H_q(V, V(K_0))$ on the left of (V) is the mapping π introduced in §2, and so the remarks just made, along with the commutativity of (2), imply that $\mathrm{loc} L_0 = \pi$, as was asserted in §2.

The proofs of Theorems 41 and 42 can now be carried out. First, to prove Theorem 41, let $\bar{\alpha}$ be an element of $H_{r-1}(V_0, P)$, and let ∂ be the boundary homomorphism of $H_{r+1}(V, V(K_0)) \to H_r(V(K_0), V_0)$. Then it must be shown that $\partial \mathrm{loc} \bar{\alpha} = 0$ if and only if $\bar{\alpha}$ is invariant. To do this a formula for $\partial \mathrm{loc} \bar{\alpha}$ will be worked out. Write $_i (\bar{\Delta} i = 1, 2, \ldots, k)$ for the generators of $H_r(V(K_0), V_0)$, $\bar{\Delta}_i$ being represented, according to Theorem 19, by a relative cycle on $V(\lambda_i)$ modulo V_0. Then $\partial \mathrm{loc} \, \bar{\alpha} = \sum c_i \bar{\Delta}_i$, where the c_i are to be determined. On the other hand, let the T_i $(i = 1, 2, \ldots, k)$ be as in §1 of Chapter VI, let the λ_i be numbered anticlockwise as they radiate from z_0, and write $\bar{\alpha}^{(i)} = T_{i-1} T_{i-2} \ldots T_1(\bar{\alpha})$. Also let ∂' be the boundary homomorphism of $H_r(V(K_0), V_0) \to H_{r-1}(V_0, P)$. Then, noting that the definition of loc depends effectively on representing $H_q(V, V(K_0))$ as a tensor product

$$H_{q-2}(V_0, P) \otimes H_2(S, K_0)$$

it is clear that $\partial \mathrm{loc} \bar{\alpha} = \sum \bar{\beta}_i$, where $\bar{\beta}_i$ is an element of the injection image of $H_r(V(\lambda_i), V_0)$ in $H_r(V(K_0), V_0)$ such that $\partial' \bar{\beta}_i = T_i(\bar{\alpha}^{(i)}) - \bar{\alpha}^{(i)} = -(\alpha^{(i)} \cdot \delta_i)\delta_i$, the last equality following from Theorem 37. Remembering that $H_r(V(K_0), V_0)$ is the direct sum of the injection images of the $H_r(V(\lambda_i), V_0)$, it follows that $c_i \bar{\delta}_i = -(\alpha^{(i)} \cdot \delta_i)\bar{\delta}_i$ for each i.

If, now, for some i, $\delta_i \neq 0$, it follows at once that, for that value of i, $c_i = -(\alpha^{(i)} \cdot \delta_i)$. On the other hand, if $\bar{\delta}_i = 0$, it will now be shown that c_i can still be taken as $-(\alpha^{(i)} \cdot \delta_i)$, namely zero, since by the lemma of §4, p.103, δ_i is homologous zero if it is homologous to zero modulo P. To establish this to point, write $c_i = f_i(\alpha^{(i)})$; then it follows that f_i is a linear function on the $(r - 1)$-cycles of V_0. The argument of §1, Chapter VI, may be repeated to show that f_i can be extended to a cocycle on V_0 which is zero on all simplexes outside a neighbourhood of the singular point on $V(z_i)$, if z_0 is near enough to z_i (a temporary adjustment which makes no essential difference). And so as in §1 of Chapter VI, it follows that $c_i = c(\alpha^{(i)} . \delta_i) = 0$, as required. It should be noted that assumption $\delta \neq 0$ which was introduced in §1 of Chapter VI, was made because the $f(\bar{\gamma})$ of that section appeared first as the coefficient of δ; here the values of f_i appear first as the coefficients of $\bar{\Delta}_i$, which is known to be non-zero, thus making any supplementary conditions unnecessary here.

The formula $\partial \mathrm{loc}\bar{\alpha} = -\sum(\alpha^{(i)} . \delta_i)\bar{\Delta}_i$ has thus been established. Then, remembering that the $\bar{\Delta}_i$ are linearly independent in $H_r(V(K_0), V_0)$ and using Theorem 37, Theorem 41 follows at once.

It is worth noting at this point another consequence of the formula just established for $\partial \mathrm{loc}\bar{\alpha}$, which gives a means of finding relations between the generators of $H_r(V, V_0)$, namely:

THEOREM 49. *Writing the $\bar{\Delta}_i$ as the generators of $H_r(V(K_0), V_0)$ and taking i to be the homomorphism of $H_r(V(K_0), V_0)$ into $H_r(V, V_0)$ induced by inclusion, then $i(\sum c_i\bar{\Delta}_i) = 0$ if and only if $c_i = -(\alpha^{(i)} . \delta_i)$ for some $\bar{\alpha} \in H_{r-1}(V_0, P)$ and for a suitable ordering of the z_i.*

PROOF. For $i(\sum c_i\bar{\Delta}_i) = 0$ if and only if $\sum c_i\bar{\Delta}_i$ is in the image of the boundary homomorphism $\partial : H_{r+1}(V, V(K_0)) \rightarrow H_r(V(K_0), V_0)$; that is to say, loc being an isomorphism onto, if and only if it is of the form $\partial \mathrm{loc}\bar{\alpha}$ for some $\bar{\alpha} \in H_{r-1}(V_0, P)$. This is equivalent to the result wanted.

Theorem 42 will now be proved. Since, as has been shown earlier in this section, $\mathrm{loc}L_0 = \pi$, it follows that, for any $\alpha \in H_{r+1}(V, V_0)$, $\mathrm{loc}L_0\alpha$ is in the image of π; and so, by Theorem 41, $L_0\alpha$ is invariant. Thus the image of L_0 is contained in the group of invariant elements in $H_{r-1}(V_0, P)$. Conversely, let β be an invariant element of $H_{r-1}(V_0, P)$. Then by Theorem 41, $\mathrm{loc}\beta = \pi\gamma$, for some $\gamma \in H_{r+1}(V, V_0)$. Using again the formula $\mathrm{loc}L_0 = \pi$, it follows that $\mathrm{loc}\beta = \mathrm{loc}L\gamma_0$, and so, since loc is an isomorphism, $\beta = L_0\gamma$. That is to say any invariant element of $H_{r-1}(V_0, P)$ is in the image of L_0. The proof of Theorem 42 is thus completed, and with it the verifications of the details of results given in §2.

REFERENCES

1. N. BOURBAKI: *Topologie Générale*, Chapter 1 (Hermann, Paris, 1940).
2. S. S. CAIRNS: Normal coordinates for extremals transversal to a manifold. *Amer. J. Math.* **60** (1938) 423–435.
3. W. L. CHOW: On the fundamental group of an algebraic variety. *Amer. J. Math.* **74** (1952) 726–736.
4. S. EILENBERG and N. E. STEENROD: *Foundations of algebraic topology* (Princeton, 1952).
5. I. FARY: Cohomologie des variétés algébriques. *Annals of Math* **65** (1957) 21–73.
6. W. V. D. HODGE: *The theory and applications of harmonic integrals*, 2nd edition, (Cambridge, England, 1952).
7. W. V. D. HODGE: The topological invariants of algebraic varieties. *Proceedings of the International Congress of Mathematicians* (Cambridge, U.S.A., 1950).
8. S. T. HU: An exposition of the relative homotopy theory. *Duke Math. J.* **14** (1947) 991–1033.
9. S. LEFSCHETZ: *L'analysis situs et la géométrie algébrique* (Gauthier-Villars, Paris, 1924).
10. N. E. STEENROD: *The topology of fibre bundles* (Princeton, 1951).
11. A. H. WALLACE: Homology theory on algebraic varieties. *Annals of Math.* **63** (1956) 248–271.
12. A. WEIL: Sur la théorie des formes différentielles attachées a une variété analytique complexe. *Comm. Math. Helv.* **20** (1947) 110–116.
13. O. ZARISKI: Algebraic surfaces. *Ergebnisse der Mathematik*, **3**, no. 5; (also Chelsea, New York, 1948).